Building Benches and Measuring Tools
Introduction to Fractions

Catherine Twomey Fosnot
Carol Marsiglio

New Perspectives on Learning, LLC
1194 Ocean Avenue
New London, CT 06320

ISBN-13: 978-0-9976886-7-2

Table of Contents

Unit Overview

The focus of this unit is the introduction of landmark fractions and fraction equivalence. The unit begins with the introduction (or re-introduction) of Tamika and Tanisha—two girls who love carpentry and are constantly engaged in building and measuring things. If students have worked with the unit *Tanisha and Tamika's Toolbox* previously (a grade 2 unit), they will likely remember how Tanisha and Tamika used measuring tapes to help design and build a toolbox with Tanisha's dad, Mr. Arnold. In first or second grade your students may also have been introduced to the girls in the unit *Measuring for the Art Show*, but it is not necessary to have done either of these earlier units first. The purpose of *Tanisha and Tamika's Toolbox* was to introduce standard units of linear measure—the yard, foot, and inch, and the meter and centimeter. The purpose of *Measuring for the Art Show* was to introduce the open number line model. In contrast, the purpose of this unit is to introduce fractions within the context of linear measurement.

In this unit students will face the dilemma of measuring lengths which are a little longer or a little shorter than exact multiples of feet. Determining the exact measurements of these lengths presents challenges that support the development of 1/2, 1/4, 3/4 and other landmark fractions, as well as an early understanding of fraction equivalence. The unit also makes use of the double number line model to support a strong sense of equivalence and to provide a potential challenge to those interested in exploring ways to convert equivalent fractions, for example how 1/2 of a foot can also be thought of as 6 out of 12 inches and how 1/2 of 1/2 produces 1/4 and therefore 2 x 1/4 = 2/4 = 1/2. The unit is aligned with the CCSS Standards of Mathematical Practice and the following core objectives:

Develop understanding of fractions as numbers.

CCSS.Math.Content.3.NF.A.1

Understand a fraction 1/*b* as the quantity formed by 1 part when a whole is partitioned into *b* equal parts; understand a fraction *a*/*b* as the quantity formed by *a* parts of size 1/*b*.

CCSS.Math.Content.3.NF.A.2

Understand a fraction as a number on the number line; represent fractions on a number line diagram.

CCSS.Math.Content.3.NF.A.2.a

Represent a fraction 1/*b* on a number line diagram by defining the interval from 0 to 1 as the whole and partitioning it into *b* equal parts. Recognize that each part has size 1/*b* and that the endpoint of the part based at 0 locates the number 1/*b* on the number line.

CCSS.Math.Content.3.NF.A.2.b

Represent a fraction *a/b* on a number line diagram by marking off lengths 1/*b* from 0. Recognize that the resulting interval has size *a/b* and that its endpoint locates the number *a/b* on the number line.

CCSS.Math.Content.3.NF.A.3

Explain equivalence of fractions in special cases, and compare fractions by reasoning about their size.

CCSS.Math.Content.3.NF.A.3.a

Understand two fractions as equivalent (equal) if they are the same size, or the same point on a number line.

CCSS.Math.Content.3.NF.A.3.b

Recognize and generate simple equivalent fractions, e.g., 1/2 = 2/4, 4/6 = 2/3. Explain why the fractions are equivalent, e.g., by using a visual fraction model.

CCSS.Math.Content.3.NF.A.3.c

Express whole numbers as fractions, and recognize fractions that are equivalent to whole numbers. *Examples: Express 3 in the form 3 = 3/1; recognize that 6/1 = 6; locate 4/4 and 1 at the same point of a number line diagram.*

CCSS.Math.Content.3.NF.A.3.d

Compare two fractions with the same numerator or the same denominator by reasoning about their size. Recognize that comparisons are valid only when the two fractions refer to the same whole. Record the results of comparisons with the symbols >, =, or <, and justify the conclusions, e.g., by using a visual fraction model.

Represent and interpret data.

CCSS.Math.Content.3.MD.B.4

Generate measurement data by measuring lengths using rulers marked with halves and fourths of an inch. Show the data by making a line plot, where the horizontal scale is marked off in appropriate units— whole numbers, halves, or quarters.

The Landscape of Learning

BIG IDEAS
❖ Larger units can encompass (and be decomposed into) smaller units
❖ Fractions may represent division with a quotient less than one
❖ With unit fractions, the greater the denominator, the smaller the piece is
❖ Part/whole integration: lengths can be added and subtracted
❖ Equivalent measurements can be exchanged
❖ Fractions express relationships; the size or amount of the whole matters
❖ To compare fractions the whole must be the same

STRATEGIES
❖ Uses standard units and estimates
❖ Decomposes unit into smaller units using estimation
❖ Decomposes unit into smaller units using halving
❖ Decomposes unit into smaller units using division
❖ Uses a common whole to compare fractions

MODELS
❖ Ruler/ Inches
❖ Open Number Line
❖ Double Number Line

The Mathematical Landscape

Building Benches and Measuring Tools: Introduction to Fractions is designed to support the development of fractions within the context of linear measurement. By second grade, most children have become competent in measuring length using a single unit end-to-end without gaps. As they measure lengths that are a little more and a little less than the foot, children experience the insufficiency of estimating and they begin to decompose the unit. In doing so they construct portions of a unit and generate how units can be decomposed further into equal parts—fractional pieces of the original unit.

Have you ever watched students trying to fold a strip of paper into thirds? Because this is so difficult to do, they often make three equal pieces by first folding as best they can. Then they snip off the sliver of the strip that remains and declare they have made thirds! Of course, they have changed the whole so they do not have 1/3 of the original strip, just three congruent pieces with part of the strip thrown away! Constructing the idea that fractions are relations and thus the size or the amount of the whole matters is an important big idea underlying an understanding of fractions. The misconception, that removing a small piece doesn't matter, results from fractions being taught as a shading activity of part/whole relations divorced from division. Research by Leen Streefland (1991) of the Freudenthal Institute in the Netherlands has shown that learners will develop a deeper understanding of fractions if they start by exploring fractions as division—fair sharing by dividing something into equal pieces. The context of measurement is used throughout this unit to enable children to construct an understanding of the division of measurement units into smaller but equal units. Fractional pieces can then be named and placed on a number line, supporting children to connect fractions as numbers on a number line and also as division where the quotient is less than 1. To coordinate these understandings, though, a complex network of relations is needed comprised of big ideas, strategies, and models as shown on the Landscape of Learning for Systems of Measurement on page 10 and the Landscape of Learning for Fractions, Decimals, and Percents on page 11.

BIG IDEAS

As young children explore the investigations within the unit, several big ideas will likely arise. These include:

- ❖ *Larger units can encompass (and be decomposed into) smaller units*
- ❖ *Fractions may represent division with a quotient less than one*
- ❖ *With unit fractions, the greater the denominator, the smaller the piece is*
- ❖ *Part/whole integration: lengths can be added and subtracted*
- ❖ *Equivalent measurements can be exchanged*
- ❖ *Fractions express relationships; the size or amount of the whole matters*
- ❖ *To compare fractions the whole must be the same*

❖ *Larger units can encompass (and be decomposed into) smaller units*

Iterated smaller units (like inches or centimeters) can be grouped into larger units (like feet or meters). On the other hand, a unit may need to be decomposed rather than grouped for exactness. For example, measuring something less than an inch requires decomposing the unit into fractional pieces.

❖ *Fractions may represent division with a quotient less than one*

Just as there are different ways of thinking about division, there are different ways of thinking about fractions. For example, 12 cookies shared among 3 children is $12/3 = 4$. This example is a fair sharing model—a rate, which is a partitive form of division: 12 for 3, or 4 for 1. The rates are equal. The problem "12 cookies, 3 to a bag, how many bags?" can also be represented as $12/3$. But this example requires us to think about measurement—a ratio of part to parts—which is a part/whole model. How many times does a group of 3 fit into 12? This is a quotative form of division. Fractions can be thought of similarly. As children divide a measurement unit into equal smaller sections they are experiencing fair sharing: 1 divided ("fair shared") by 4 = 1/4. They also experience a fraction as measurement: 1 out of 4 equivalent pieces. One might ask how many times 4 fits into 1? Only 1/4 of it fits.

❖ With unit fractions, the greater the denominator, the smaller the piece is

Initially students may think that unit fractions with greater denominators represent greater amounts because they attempt to generalize their knowledge of whole number to fractions. For example, they reason that since 8 is greater than 7, 1/8 must be greater than 1/7. After all, it has more parts! As students are introduced to fractions in division contexts like breaking a measurement unit into smaller pieces, it becomes easier for them to understand why the greater the denominator, the smaller the piece is.

❖ Part/whole integration: lengths can be added and subtracted

It is the integration of the smaller units with the whole into a part/whole structure that supports children to come to realize that fractional lengths can be added and subtracted: 1/4 + 1/4 + 1/4 = 3/4; and 1/4 remains in the whole.

❖ Equivalent measurements can be exchanged

Once children construct conservation of length and unitizing and have had ample opportunities to work with a variety of measurement units, they begin to understand that various units can be used to describe length and distance, and that equivalent pieces can be exchanged.

❖ Fractions express relationships; the size or amount of the whole matters

Fractions can be thought of as numbers but they can also be relations. The whole matters. For example, 1/8 could actually be more than 1/4 if we are talking about 1/8 of a yard versus 1/4 of a foot. 1/2 of a meter is longer than 1/2 of a foot. Once this big idea is constructed, students come to understand that a common whole is needed to compare fractions.

❖ To compare fractions the whole must be the same

When fractions are thought of as numbers, a point on a number line between 0 and 1, the whole is common. It is 1. This understanding allows for the generating of another big idea: if you have a common whole you can compare the relative position or size of two numbers. For example, to compare 1/4 to 1/2, you only need to look at the denominators because the numerators are the same. To compare 1/4 to 2/4 you only need to look at the numerators because the denominators are the same.

As you work with the activities in this unit, you will notice that students will use many strategies to solve the problems that are posed to them. Here are some strategies to notice:

❖ *Uses standard units and estimates*
❖ *Decomposes unit into smaller units using estimation*
❖ *Decomposes unit into smaller units using halving*
❖ *Decomposes unit into smaller units using division*
❖ *Uses a common whole to compare fractions*

❖ *Uses standard unit and estimates*

When children first start using measurement tools, they treat the unit as a whole and measure end to end. When they discover the tool is too short, they report that the length is a little bit more. They estimate rather than determining an exact measure. For example, when measuring a length of 14 inches with a ruler, they report that it is a little bit longer than a foot.

❖ *Decomposes unit into smaller units using estimation*

Precisely because most contexts demand exact measurements (building a bench with only approximate measurements would likely result in an inexact length that won't fit!), measurement units, to be useful, may need to be decomposed into smaller units. When trying to decompose a foot into smaller equal fractional parts, children will often begin by using perception alone. They estimate where some smaller marks might go, often erasing several times trying to adjust to make the intervals equal, eventually becoming satisfied with their adjustments. They have made approximate smaller pieces, but they have not divided the unit fairly into equivalent pieces.

❖ *Decomposes unit into smaller units by halving*

Decomposing by estimating and adjusting, however, is not sustainable. The need for exactness when measuring is important, and children tire of drawing and erasing. They seek out other strategies. In this unit, we provide children with foot-long paper strips, a medium that supports the evolution of some further strategies using folding. Children usually halve, then halve again to make fourths, and then halve again to make eighths. This will be a nice strategy eventually to understand the fractional inch markers on a ruler, but making eighths of a foot is not very helpful for finding 12 inches, as the eighth is 1.5 inches. This creates a new dilemma as children grapple to find 12 equal inches on their strips. Breaking the 3 inches up into 3 equal pieces by folding is difficult. Be prepared to see some children wanting to trim their foot-long piece when their folding does not result in 3 equal pieces! This is a nice moment to revisit measurement. You might ask, "Would the foot-long piece still measure exactly one foot, or would the whole measurement now be off? You do have 3 equal pieces, but is this piece 1/3 of the 3 inches you started with?"

❖ *Decomposes unit into smaller units using division*

As children decompose units they eventually construct the idea that they are dividing the unit into equal parts. This is a nice place to introduce fraction notation naturally: one foot divided into two equal parts is 1/2; thus 6 inches is 1/2 of a foot. One inch is 1/12 of a foot. The bar in fraction notation indicates division.

❖ *Uses a common whole to compare fractions*

Recognizing that fractions of the same whole can be compared, students make use of common numerators or common denominators to compare the position or size of fractions.

MATHEMATICAL MODELING

Model of a situation

Initially models emerge as a representation *of* a situation; later they are used by teachers to represent children's computation strategies. Ultimately, models are appropriated by children as powerful tools *for* thinking (Gravemeijer, 1999). In this unit children engage in constructing fractional units and placing them on measurement tools. They use paper strips as a bar model and eventually open number lines to represent the composition and decomposition of units. The double open number line model is introduced as a representation of the tools students produce to further explore equivalence and substitution.

The open number line encourages a linear representation of numbers and number operations for children that is powerful for developing mental arithmetic strategies (Beishuizen 1993; Klein, Beishuizen, and Treffers 2002). In this unit, the open number line is used as a double number line where both the whole unit and the fractional pieces can be shown. It is a model that also supports children to understand how fractions are numbers between 0 and 1, but how they can also be seen as operators: 1/2 of 12 = 6.

Model of Student Strategies

Children benefit from seeing the teacher model their strategies on an open number line. Once the model has emerged as a representation of the situation, you can use it to model the children's strategies as they engage in minilessons. Notes are provided within the unit to help you do this, but if your school has purchased P2S2: a Personalized Professional Support System™ from New Perspectives Online (www.NewPerspectivesOnline.net), you will find it very helpful to go to modules in *Digging Deep: Minilessons and Representations* where Cathy explains in depth how to do this and where you can see videos of teachers doing minilessons with their children.

Model as a Tool for Thinking

Eventually children will be able to use the open number line as a representational tool for thinking about measurement. They will be able to imagine fractions as numbers on a number line and mentally mark lengths (and jumps) in various configurations. They will understand how equivalent length sections can be exchanged and how 1/2 of a foot (or meter) is different than 1/2 of an inch (or centimeter). They will also have become skilled length measurers: measuring competently, knowing the need for identical units and the relationship between units, knowing how to partition units into smaller equal parts, and how to exchange units to produce overall lengths. And perhaps more important to the goals of this unit, they will have constructed several big ideas about fractions.

Graphics of the full landscapes of learning for this unit are provided on pages 10 and 11. The purpose of these graphics is to allow you to see the longer journey of students' development as they work with measurement and fractions and to place your work with this unit within the scope of this long-term development. You may also find the graphics helpful as a way to record the progress of individual students for yourself. Each landmark can be shaded in as you find evidence in a student's work and in what the student says—evidence that a landmark strategy, big idea, or way of modeling has been constructed. Or, you may prefer to use our web-based app (www.NewPerspectivesOnAssessment.com) to document your children's growth digitally. In a very real sense, you will be recording the individual pathways your students take as they develop as young mathematicians.

References and Resources

Gravemeijer, Koeno P. E. 1999. How emergent models may foster the constitution of formal mathematics. *Mathematical Thinking and Learning 1* (2): 155–77.

Klein, Anton S., Meindert Beishuizen, and Adri Treffers. 2002. The empty number line in Dutch second grade, In *Lessons learned from research,* eds. Judith Sowder and Bonnie Schapelle. Reston, VA: NCTM.

Sarama, Julie and Douglas Clements, Jeffrey Barrett, Douglas W. Van Dine, Jennifer S. McDonel (2011). Evaluation of a learning trajectory for length in the early years. *Mathematics Education.* 43: 667-680.

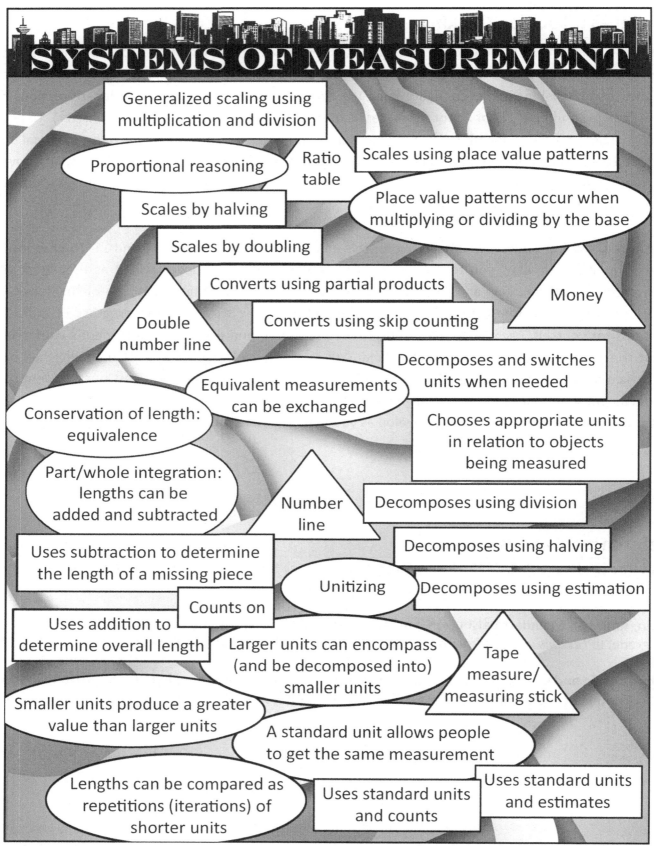

SYSTEMS OF MEASUREMENT

Generalized scaling using multiplication and division

Proportional reasoning

Ratio table

Scales using place value patterns

Scales by halving

Place value patterns occur when multiplying or dividing by the base

Scales by doubling

Converts using partial products

Money

Double number line

Converts using skip counting

Decomposes and switches units when needed

Equivalent measurements can be exchanged

Chooses appropriate units in relation to objects being measured

Conservation of length: equivalence

Part/whole integration: lengths can be added and subtracted

Number line

Decomposes using division

Uses subtraction to determine the length of a missing piece

Decomposes using halving

Counts on

Unitizing

Decomposes using estimation

Uses addition to determine overall length

Larger units can encompass (and be decomposed into) smaller units

Tape measure/ measuring stick

Smaller units produce a greater value than larger units

A standard unit allows people to get the same measurement

Lengths can be compared as repetitions (iterations) of shorter units

Uses standard units and counts

Uses standard units and estimates

The landscape of learning: systems of measurement on the horizon showing landmark strategies (rectangles), big ideas (ovals), and models (triangles).

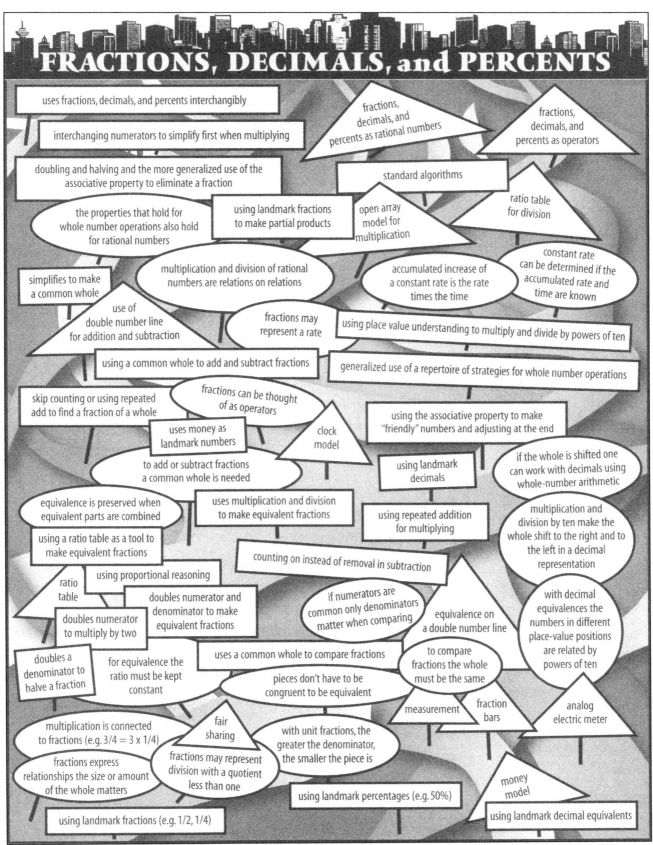

FRACTIONS, DECIMALS, and PERCENTS

uses fractions, decimals, and percents interchangibly

interchanging numerators to simplify first when multiplying

fractions, decimals, and percents as rational numbers

fractions, decimals, and percents as operators

doubling and halving and the more generalized use of the associative property to eliminate a fraction

standard algorithms

ratio table for division

the properties that hold for whole number operations also hold for rational numbers

using landmark fractions to make partial products

open array model for multiplication

constant rate can be determined if the accumulated rate and time are known

simplifies to make a common whole

multiplication and division of rational numbers are relations on relations

accumulated increase of a constant rate is the rate times the time

use of double number line for addition and subtraction

fractions may represent a rate

using place value understanding to multiply and divide by powers of ten

using a common whole to add and subtract fractions

generalized use of a repertoire of strategies for whole number operations

skip counting or using repeated add to find a fraction of a whole

fractions can be thought of as operators

using the associative property to make "friendly" numbers and adjusting at the end

uses money as landmark numbers

clock model

if the whole is shifted one can work with decimals using whole-number arithmetic

to add or subtract fractions a common whole is needed

using landmark decimals

multiplication and division by ten make the whole shift to the right and to the left in a decimal representation

equivalence is preserved when equivalent parts are combined

uses multiplication and division to make equivalent fractions

using repeated addition for multiplying

using a ratio table as a tool to make equivalent fractions

counting on instead of removal in subtraction

with decimal equivalences the numbers in different place-value positions are related by powers of ten

ratio table

using proportional reasoning

doubles numerator and denominator to make equivalent fractions

if numerators are common only denominators matter when comparing

equivalence on a double number line

doubles numerator to multiply by two

doubles a denominator to halve a fraction

for equivalence the ratio must be kept constant

uses a common whole to compare fractions

to compare fractions the whole must be the same

analog electric meter

pieces don't have to be congruent to be equivalent

measurement

fraction bars

multiplication is connected to fractions (e.g. 3/4 = 3 x 1/4)

fair sharing

with unit fractions, the greater the denominator, the smaller the piece is

fractions express relationships the size or amount of the whole matters

fractions may represent division with a quotient less than one

money model

using landmark percentages (e.g. 50%)

using landmark fractions (e.g. 1/2, 1/4)

using landmark decimal equivalents

The landscape of learning: fractions, decimals, and percents on the horizon showing landmark strategies (rectangles), big ideas (ovals), and models (triangles).

DAY ONE

MEASURING THE FIRST BENCH

Materials Needed

A 12" section of adding machine paper, measured and cut carefully (one per pair of students, but have a few extras available)

A 66" section of adding machine paper, measured and cut carefully (one per pair of students)

One ruler showing the 12 inches

Building Benches (Appendix A)

Pencils and Markers

Several sheets of copy or drawing paper

Blank Chart Paper for posters

In this unit, children engage in measuring lengths of boards for benches to be built in the meeting area. The story can be told as if two girls in another class, Tamika and Tanisha, are helping their teacher get the measurements to bring to the lumberyard for the purchasing and cutting of the boards. Alternately, you and your students can actually build benches for your classroom. On Day One, your students will engage in the same investigation as the two girls in the story (or they will do it for you). They will use a 12-inch (1-foot) section of adding machine paper as a measurement tool, and measure the length of a longer strip of adding machine paper, which represents the desired length of the bench.

Day One Outline

Developing the Context
❖ Read the story *Building Benches* (Appendix A).
❖ Explain that the short strip is exactly 1 foot, which is also 12 inches. Use the ruler to demonstrate this but then put the ruler away. **DO NOT provide rulers for the students.** Having only the paper strip as a tool is a critical part of the investigation.
❖ Explain to students that the long strip of paper is the blueprint—the desired length for the bench. Have them work in pairs using the foot-long strip to figure out the length of the bench.

Supporting the Investigation
❖ Confer with children as they work, noting the strategies they use as they measure. As students finish, ask them to prepare a poster to convince others of their solutions and important things they have noticed about measurement. These posters will be used on Day Two in a gallery walk and math congress.

Developing the Context

Gather your students together and read the story *Building Benches* (Appendix A) to them. As an alternative to using the story in Appendix A, if you have a woodworking teacher you might consider building real benches for your meeting area. Rather than telling the story of the two girls you might just explain that you need benches for the meeting area and the woodworking teacher has agreed to cut the boards if he is provided with the exact measurements needed.

Tech Tip

To develop the context, many teachers take a photo of Appendix A with a cell phone or iPad and project it. Others use a document camera to project the page onto a whiteboard or screen. If you don't have the technology for any of these options, you can also just read the story.

After developing the context, explain that the task for the day is to figure out how long the bench is, what length boards to buy, and where the cuts should be. **Don't tell students how long the 66-inch strip is.** This is what you want them to figure out. Just pass out the tools (the foot-long strip and the 66-inch strip representing the length of the bench). Assign math partners and send students off to figure out the length of the bench using the strip. **DO NOT pass out rulers** even if students request them. The strip is a critical constraint to the investigation. You will likely find that many of your students will fold the strip in half and report that the bench is 5 $\frac{1}{2}$ feet. This would not happen if you passed out rulers. Everyone would just measure in inches.

Teacher Note: How to Build the Benches

The benches are easy to make. Each bench is made with two 1" x 6" boards cut to the size the children measure. The first bench is 66" long, the second and third are 63" and 64" respectively. The three bench planks are arranged in a u-shape and placed on milk carton crates. Most lumberyards will do the cutting free (or for a nominal fee) and many sell wooden milk crates that can be screwed right to the planks. Some school cafeterias actually give away the plastic crates, however, so you might ask them first. If you want durable soft benches you can also staple inexpensive carpet padding onto the planks and then cover them with fabric.

Supporting the Investigation

As students begin to work, note first with a quick look around if all students are engaged and understand the context. Work first to ensure students understand the context and then sit and confer with a few pairs as they work.

Some students may decide to measure using the foot as their unit. Note if they iterate the strip and carefully mark the end each time, leaving no gaps. If not, ask them if exactness matters. Could their length be a little too long, or a little too short? Support them to consider how exactness really matters for the bench to fit. After 5 iterations (producing 5 feet) they will have a smaller section left. If they fold the strip in half, this is an opportunity to introduce fractions as division: one strip divided into two equal pieces is represented as 1/2. As you write the symbolic notation explain that the bar means to divide. But then ask students what they should tell the lumberyard. 5 $\frac{1}{2}$ of what? Will they need to give the employee the strip? Support students to remember that the size of the strip is 1 foot and that 1/2 of the strip is 1/2 of 1 foot. Encourage them to explain their thinking. (See Figure 1.)

Figure 1: A work sample showing the folding to get 1/2.

Other students may start with inches. They may then use repeated addition, 12 + 12 + 12 + 12 + 12 + 6, noting that the remainder is only 6 inches more, not a full foot. Ask how they got the 6 inches. They probably did 1/2 of 12 and knew it was 6. The remainder can then be represented as 6 out of 12 inches, or 6/12. This fraction can also be described as division by explaining that the foot can be thought of as 1 whole divided into 12 parts: 1/12. The fraction 6/12 is then 6 x 1/12, since each 1/12 is one inch and there are 6 of them. (See Figure 2.)

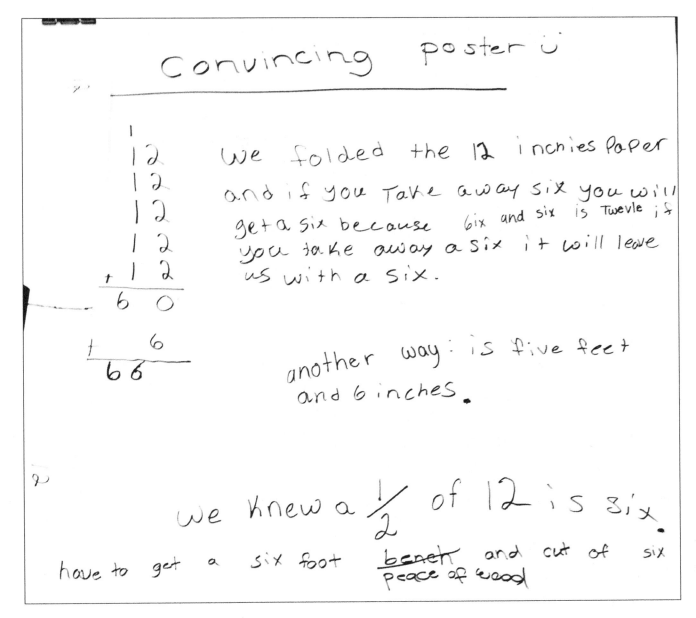

Figure 2: A work sample using the inches.

Behind the Numbers

Providing only a blank 12" strip was a conscious decision in the design of this unit. Precisely because it is blank, children will likely fold the strip to measure and mark the extra 6" needed. Some may fold it and then try to make marks on the paper. Either way what will likely arise is an opportunity to discuss how 1 strip (or foot) divided into 2 equal pieces can be represented as 1/2. There are 60 inches, which is 5 whole feet, plus 1/2 or 6/12 of a foot more. As children use different strategies and tools, equivalence will also come up: 6" out of 12" = 6/12 = 1/2 of a foot. These ideas are important big ideas on the landscape described in the overview. They will provide for a rich discussion in the gallery walk and math congress, which will be held on Day Two.

Inside One Classroom: Conferring with Students at Work

Carol (the teacher): I've been watching what you two are doing and it looks like such an interesting strategy. Can I sit and confer with you?

Alyssa: Sure.

Jake: We measured with the strips and we got 5 feet, but it wasn't long enough. This is the mark where the 5 feet ended. This part is 60 inches.

Carol: So you had to figure out how long this end section was. Tell me what you were doing with the smaller strip. It looked like you were folding it.

Alyssa: We looked at the part that was left and it looked like it might be about half of this smaller strip, so we are folding to see if it is.

Jake: It is! See, it fits exactly. So the length of the bench needs to be 60 inches and 1/2 of the strip.

Carol: Wow! Folding! What a great strategy! One strip divided into two equal parts by folding! And you are right. That is ½. The bar means to divide. 1 divided by 2 is 1/2. Very exciting! But now I have a question. The boards at lumberyards are sold in feet. They come in 6, 8, or 10-foot lengths. What length boards should I buy and where should the lumberyard cut? I don't think I can tell the employee 60 inches and 1/2 of a strip. *(Both students are now quiet, puzzled and pondering the question.)*

Jake: The strip is a foot. So the bench is 5 $\frac{1}{2}$ feet.

Carol: What do you think Alyssa? Is Jake right?

Alyssa: Yes, but the foot is 12 inches, so 1/2 of 12 is 6 inches.

Carol: Wow! So now I have another question. Alyssa, you said this piece is 6 inches and that a foot was 12 inches. If the foot is broken into 12 equal pieces, is the inch 1/12 of a foot? And is the half then equal to 6/12? So can this piece, which you and Jake have proven is 1/2 of a foot, also be thought of as 6 x 1/12?

Author's notes

Carol notes that the pair is folding the strip. She sits to confer because this strategy will likely result in the generation of fractions and she wants to support that—and it will give her a chance to introduce the common notation and talk about division with her students.

Note how Carol's conferral is characterized by cycles of listening, celebrating, and challenging.

These are big ideas for these young mathematicians and Carol celebrates with them again and then leaves them with another challenge.

As students begin to reach conclusions about the length of the board, ask them to prepare posters presenting their findings for a gallery walk and math congress on Day Two. Explain that mathematicians often want to share and justify their findings with each other, and that when they do they are careful to choose the most important ideas to share. They build arguments to convince others they are right.

Towards the aim of developing their ability to write viable arguments you might encourage your students to record how their thinking changed and the interesting connections they noticed, and to think about how they will convince their peers that they are right.

Reflections on the Day

Today students were asked to measure an object longer than 5 feet, but shorter than 6 feet. They were asked to find a part of a unit and did so by decomposing it into fractional pieces. They may have used inches and gotten 6 out of 12 inches. This provided an opportunity to discuss the idea of an inch as 1/12 of a foot and 6/12 as 6 x 1/12. Others may have folded the 1-foot strip into two equal pieces and this strategy brought about the emergence of the notion of a fractional piece as the division of a unit into equal pieces. Along the way your students likely discussed 1/2 as a number halfway between 0 and 1. Tomorrow a math congress will provide an opportunity for a rich discussion on all of these ideas and in particular how fractions result when a whole is divided into equal pieces and how fractions are also a part/parts relation.

DAY TWO

THE LENGTH OF THE BENCH

Today begins with a minilesson using a string of related problems designed to support the relationship between multiplication and division, specifically halving (division by 2) and doubling (multiplication by 2). After the minilesson, students review the posters they began on Day One, adding finishing touches if needed. A math congress ensues focused on the idea of 1/2 as the midpoint of the foot-long strip, and as a number between 0 and 1 that is produced when 1 is divided by 2.

Day Two Outline

Minilesson: A String of Related Problems

❖ A string of related problems encourages a discussion on the relationship of division and multiplication by 2.

Facilitating the Gallery Walk

❖ Confer with children as they put finishing touches to their posters, asking them to consider the most important things they want to tell their audience.

❖ Review expectations for helpful comments and feedback.

❖ Conduct a gallery walk to allow students time to reflect and comment on each other's posters from Day One.

❖ Students review the feedback on their own poster.

Facilitating the Math Congress

❖ Invite students to come to the meeting area to discuss a few of the strategies used for finding the length of the bench.

❖ Focus discussion on the equivalence of 6/12 of a foot to 1/2 of a foot and the equivalence of $5\frac{1}{2}$ feet to 66 inches. The number 1/2 is then represented on a number line as the number midway between 0 and 1 and as the quotient of 1 divided by 2.

Materials Needed

Sticky notes (two or three per student)

Students' work from Day One

Pencils

Minilesson: A string of related problems

This string is designed with several related problems to provide students with opportunities to explore the relationship between multiplication and division. Do one problem at a time, representing students' thinking using an open number line.

The String:
10 ÷ 2
2 x 5
5 x 2
20 ÷ 2
4 ÷ 2
24 ÷ 2
2 x 12
30 ÷ 2
15 x 2

Behind the Numbers

Students may think of 10 ÷ 2 in two different ways. Some may think of it quotatively, asking themselves how many 2s fit into 10. To represent this strategy on the open number line draw 5 groups of 2 as shown below.

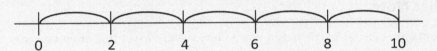

Others may think of 10 ÷ 2 as fair-sharing or partitioning 10, making 2 equal groups of 5, with 5 as the midpoint of the distance between 0 and 10.

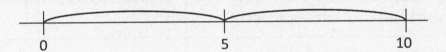

Both approaches are correct, and the different representations will enable students to explore several relationships: how 1/2 of 10 equals 5; how 5/10 = 1/2; and the connection between multiplication and division. The first representation shows the multiplication of 5 groups of 2, whereas the second shows 2 groups of 5—a case of the commutative property. The two problems that follow ensure that this discussion (and the two representations) will come up if it didn't occur naturally when the first problem was discussed. The next three problems will likely generate a discussion on partial quotients: 24/2 = 20/2 + 4/2. Once again, depending on how your students think about the division, different representations may arise. Some may consider 20/2 as 2 groups of 10, and then 4/2 as 2 groups of 2. When the groups of 2 are alternated with the groups of 10, 12 is seen as the midpoint of the distance from 0 to 24. Other students may consider 20/2 as 10 groups of 2 and 4/2 as 2 groups of 2, thereby producing 12 groups of 2. The last pair of problems may invite students to make use of partial quotients, 20/2 and 10/2 = 30/2, or partial products, (2 x 10) + (2 x 5) = 2 x 15.

Facilitating the Gallery Walk

To help students prepare for a congress, hold a gallery walk first. A gallery walk is an opportunity for students to make their work public. Mathematicians not only solve problems; they also craft proofs—justifications to convince others of the validity of their statements. They publish their work and invite comments or questions from other mathematicians. The gallery walk is a chance for students, as young mathematicians at work, to engage in this process.

Display all the posters around the room and have everyone spend about fifteen minutes walking around, reading and commenting on the mathematics on the posters. Pass out sticky notes and pencils for students to write review comments and explain that they should focus on only three or four posters so that they can read carefully and provide specific, detailed suggestions for revisions to the authors. Ensure that students spread out and that every poster gets at least a few reviewer's comments. Students will be working quietly and individually at this time. As students are doing their gallery walk, you should also participate. This is a chance for you to consider which of the posters you would like your students to share during the math congress. Look for solutions that will enable group discussion on some big ideas about fractions. Give students a few minutes to read the comments and questions posted on their own work and then convene a math congress.

Teacher Note

If students have never participated in a gallery walk, expect that their comments and questions may be trivial at first. With experience, students will develop the ability to pose relevant questions and understand what kinds of comments are helpful to the creators of the posters. You may have to spend time examining the kinds of questions and comments students made on a given poster in order to help them understand what constitutes an appropriate response.

Facilitating the Math Congress

As you plan which posters to use for the math congress, look for the emergence of some of the big ideas on fractions described in the overview. For example, some students may have worked with feet and folded the smaller strip getting 1/2. This is an important idea on the landscape: fractions can be thought of as division and $1 \div 2 = 1/2$. This is a nice place to discuss how the fraction bar is just another way to write division. (See Figure 3.)

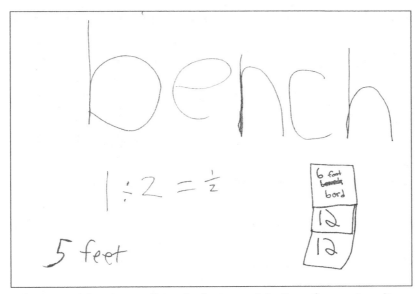

Figure 3: A sample piece of work that would allow for a nice discussion on how fractions can be thought of as division.

Some students may have measured 5 feet plus 6 inches. Be sure to include work that shows an understanding of the 6-inch piece as part of a whole foot (half of it) as this is also one of the big ideas on the landscape: understanding that larger units encompass (and can be decomposed into) smaller units. The whole foot is too big to measure the smaller remaining section, and so smaller units are needed here. The comparison between 6 inches and half a foot also gives you a chance to have the students discuss 6/12 = 1/2. (See Figure 2 in Day One.)

Another big idea on the landscape is that fractions represent division with a quotient less than one. At a certain point in the congress that seems appropriate, use a double number line to show both the feet and the inches. Explain that your line represents the 1-foot strip. On the top of the line represent 0 to 1 so you can show how 1/2 is a number halfway between 0 and 1 (the 1 represents 1 strip). The 1 in this case also represents 1 foot, so underneath the line write 0 inches at the start and 12 inches at the end. (See Figure 4.) Now 6 inches can be shown as the halfway point between 0 and 12, with 1/2 directly above it. (Fractions go above the line; whole numbers go underneath the line.) You can also write the equivalent fraction 6/12 above the line. Ask your students to consider if the mark for 6 inches out of 12 inches is the same as the mark for 1/2.

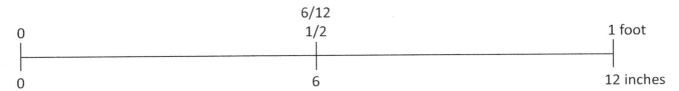

Figure 4. Representing 6/12 = 1/2 on a double number line.
[Note that fractions are on the top and whole numbers (the inches) are on the bottom.]

Inside One Classroom: A Portion of the Math Congress

Carol (the teacher): Mya, let's have you and Hayden begin. Tell us about how you solved this problem.

Mya: We measured the long strip up to 5 feet and we put a little mark there. We know the small strip is 12 inches.

Hayden: Then we put the small strip on the bench strip right next to where the 5-foot mark was. We folded it so that it was the same size as the part that was left. We know 6 + 6 = 12. So we know it was 6 inches long.

Carol: Well that is an interesting strategy. Let's see where you have drawn your strategy. I see a mark on this long strip you drew. Is this your 5-foot mark? So then you show another part here that's a different color. Is that the part that is left over?

Mya: Yes, I thought we needed to show it in a different way because it's the leftover part. So we decided to make it a different color.

Carol: Hmmm... interesting strategy. I saved your strip of paper from yesterday. I notice that you have folded it. Why did you do that?

Mya: Well we folded it into two parts, like half of the paper.

Hayden: I want to fold it again. See, it's the same size on each side. 6 + 6 = 12!

Carol: *(Holding the strip of paper and demonstrating.)* Let's see if we understand you. You used the strip and folded it in half. This made two equal pieces and each was 6 inches. Let me represent what you did on a number line, too, so we can discuss your strategy further. *(Carol draws a line segment and marks a 0 at the beginning and a 1 at the end, with the 1/2 marked at the midpoint.)* Here is a section of a number line. Imagine the one strip going to this point where I have marked 1. Turn and talk about what Mya and Hayden have done. Is this middle mark where the number 1/2 goes? Can we think about 1/2 as a number halfway between 0 and 1? They said 1 divided into 2 equal pieces is 1/2. *(After a few minutes of pair talk, Carol resumes whole group discussion.)* So, you turned and talked with an elbow partner. Did anyone have an interesting partner?

Juanita: I did. Jessie told me that the 1/2 is 1/2 of a foot, so 6 inches equals 1/2 of a foot.

Carol: What a nice connection! Hmm... We divided 1 whole into 2 equal pieces and that was 1/2 and the 6 inches out of

Author's notes

Carol starts with Mya and Hayden in the hopes that their work will be helpful in getting her class to think about fractions in two ways: as a number between 0 and 1, and as the division of 1 by 2. Their strategy is primarily addition—they have added on 6 more inches to 5 feet, but she hopes discussion on their work will engender a discussion on 1/2 because they have folded the strip into two equal pieces.

Representing a line segment from 0 to 1, where the strip is one unit, provides students with an opportunity to consider 1/2 as a number between 0 and 1—a number that can be represented on a number line.

Providing time for a "turn and talk" is critical here. Students need time to reflect at this juncture as there are several big ideas involved, and all will likely cause some cognitive reorganization. Puzzlement and discussion are required.

the 12 inches goes at the same place? Then could I also write 6/12 here, right above 1/2? Does 6/12 equal 1/2?

Hayden: *(Talks as he writes "12/2".)* We had 12 inches and we divided it into 2 pieces.

Mya: And each piece was 6 inches long...but I don't see why you wrote 6/12.

Hayden: I think maybe it just depends on how you think about it. It is 6 inches, but the foot is 12 inches, so 6 inches is the halfway point to get to 12. But it is also 1/2 of the foot. I think the bench needs to be 5 ½ feet, or 66 inches. They are the same thing.

Carol: Hayden, you wrote 12/2 and that does equal 6 like you said, not 1/2. But what you are saying about how it depends on how you think about it is very interesting. Could we think about 6 divided by 12? That's what the bar means, right? How much of the 12 fits into the 6? Let's all turn and talk again. Can we imagine 6 divided by 12?

Mya: Oh!! I get it! It doesn't even fit once! Only half of it fits! 6/12 does equal 1/2. It depends on whether you think about the foot as a whole and want to know how much of the whole it is.

Paulette: If we think about 6 feet divided into 12 equal pieces, each foot has to be cut in half, so that is 1/2 of a foot too. Like in the minilesson we did. It just depends on how you think about it.

Carol: Is this what you mean, Paulette? *(Carol draws 6 lines, and marks each as one foot. Then she cuts each line in half to make 12 pieces.)*

Paulette: Yes. I think that's 6 ÷ 12 also and the answer is 1/2. *(Several students murmur in surprise, and then agreement.)*

Carol: What part of the foot is 1 inch? Let's turn and talk about this question for a bit. *(As the students discuss this question, Carol moves around and listens in on several discussions.)*

Alton: I think if there are 12 inches in a foot... maybe 1 inch is 1/12 of a foot?

Carol: Who agrees with Alton, that 1/12 of a foot is 1 inch? *(All hands go up.)* Then is this also true: 6 x 1/12 = 6/12 = 1/2? Turn and talk about this statement. Is this a true statement?

Carol pursues some hard ideas here. 12/2 does not equal 1/2. It equals 6. She wants the discussion to be on fractions, not on whole number division. How can she focus the class on the expression 1/2=6/12? Several big ideas about fractions are at play here and they are connected to the minilesson that started math workshop today: fractions can be thought of as a part/parts relation (one part out of two), but also as 1 divided by 2. The bar can represent division.

Mya is using a quotative model to think about the division.

Paulette is thinking about division with a partitive, fairsharing model.

Carol represents Paulette's thinking. There are now 6 wholes shared into 12 equal pieces.

As a challenge, Carol puts forth one more perspective for consideration: 6/12 can be thought of as 6 x 1/12.

Reflections on the Day

Today began with a minilesson, which helped students explore various representations for division and the operation's relationship to multiplication. This minilesson also prepared students for the difficult work ahead in the congress as they grappled with new ideas about fractions. The gallery walk and math congress gave students the opportunity to publish, share, and discuss their work. They also provided a chance for children to explain and justify their thinking and to learn from others.

Think back to the overview of the unit where the landscape of learning for fractions was described. This is a nice time to look over the work your students have produced. What big ideas, strategies, and models for fractions did you see emerging in your discussions today? The measurement context helped students to consider fractions as numbers between 0 and 1. Fraction notation was connected to division and to a part/parts model of fractions. Students also engaged in proving the equivalence of 6/12 and 1/2. Take some photographs of the work your students produced and make some anecdotal records as documentation for where each student is on the landscape of learning. Each day you should see your children making progress on the landscape, but each child's pathway will likely be different. The lessons are not designed with one goal for all—one "it" for everyone to get. Each child should be learning, but most likely they are not all learning the same thing. Learning *is* development. For this reason it is helpful to document the journey of each child on individual landscapes. As you work with students over the course of this unit, they will have more opportunities to share and test ideas and strategies in the mathematical community. Their perspectives on fractions will broaden and deepen as they construct a network of relations in the days ahead.

DAY THREE

ADDITIONAL BENCHES

Materials Needed

A 12" section of adding machine paper, measured and cut carefully (one per pair of students, but have extras available)

A 63" and a 64" section of adding machine paper, measured and cut carefully (one per pair of students)

Building Benches (Appendix A)

Pencils and Markers

Several sheets of copy or drawing paper

Blank Chart Paper for posters (sticky note style is best as it makes taping on the walls unnecessary)

Today begins with another minilesson designed to focus discussion on the relationships between division and multiplication. Students may recognize the commutative property of multiplication, also. The ideas explored in the minilesson will serve as a foundation for the more complex ideas students will explore as they investigate the lengths of two new benches.

Day Three Outline

Minilesson: A string of related problems
❖ A string of related problems supports students to continue exploring the relationship between division and multiplication.

Developing the Context
❖ Pass out the one-foot strips and the two longer strips that represent the two new benches, noting that one bench is a bit shorter than the other.
❖ Send students off in pairs to figure out the lengths of the two new benches, reminding them that boards come in 6, 8, and 10-foot lengths.

Supporting the Investigation
❖ Confer with children as they work, noting the strategies they use.
❖ Support students to look for connections as they find the fractional part of the board needed for each of the two new benches. As students finish, ask them to prepare a poster to convince others of their solutions and the important things they have noticed. These posters will be used in a gallery walk and math congress tomorrow.

Minilesson: A string of related problems

This string has been carefully constructed to support learners' understanding of the relationship between division and multiplication. Use the open number line to represent students' thinking and use the fraction bar to represent division interchangeably with the division sign. Students will discover the relationships between the problems and start making use of them, likely generating a nice discussion on the commutative property of multiplication as well as the relationship between multiplication and division. Use the open number line to represent students' strategies just as you did on Day Two, with whole numbers on the bottom and fractions on the top.

The String:
3 x 8
8 x 3
24 / 8
24 / 3
6 x 4
4 x 6
24 / 4
24 / 6

Developing the Context

Explain that today everyone will help with measurements for the two side benches. Pass out the foot-long strips again, reminding students that the strips are each one foot. Once again DO NOT make rulers available. Holding the two longer strips that represent the lengths of the two new benches side-by-side, note how one is a little bit shorter than the other. **Ensure that children realize the lengths are different before you send them off, and as you move around conferring note if they have forgotten and remind them that the two benches are not the same lengths even though they are close.**

Behind the Numbers

Providing 63" and 64" strips of paper gives students the opportunity to look at different parts of the same whole (12 inches). One bench is 5 $\frac{1}{4}$ feet (63") and the other is 5 $\frac{1}{3}$ feet (64"). The work with 1/2 on Days One and Two provides a nice support to consider how 1/2 of 1/2 = 1/4 and to notice that 6/12 halved is 3/12. The juxtaposition of 63" and 64" on the same day supports children to consider the relationship between 3" and 4". They may also remember the relationships from the minilesson and note that 4 x 3 = 12, so 12/4 = 3; and thus 3/12 = 1/4. Similarly, 3 x 4 = 12, so 12/3 = 4; and thus 4/12 = 1/3. The relationship between 12/4 = 3 and 12/3 = 4 can also be explored. The idea of equivalence and the diversity of students' strategies will provide for a rich discussion in the gallery walk and congress, which will be held on Day Four.

Supporting the Investigation

Some students may start with the 63" piece of paper. If they fold the 12" strip in half as they did on Day One and they will find that 1/2 is still too long. They may then fold the strip in half again producing fourths and get the length they need. As you confer you might ask them how many equal parts they now have in the foot-long strip. If they have folded carefully they should have 4 equal parts: 1/2 of 1/2 = 1/4. Remind students how division can be represented with the fraction bar: 1 divided by 4 is 1/4. Remind them also that since the strip is 1 foot it is also 12 inches, and suggest they work to figure out how many inches 1/4 of the foot is. Exploring the inches will bring them to a consideration of the equivalence of 1/4 and 3/12. (See Figure 5.) When students examine how the half was halved, they may also note that the numerator halved (from 6 to 3), but the denominator (12) stayed the same. This is another big idea on the landscape: to halve a fraction, halve the numerator. If children start marking all of the twelfths on a bar or number line, look at whether they are marking the units of measurement (seeing the inches as lengths), or whether they are just writing fractions at each tick, missing some ticks, or have too many or not enough spaces. As you confer, have students show you how they know the mark goes where they have written it. If they have folded, have them show the folding. Examine the number of pieces they have made together and remind them that fractions mean division. 12/12 means the strip has been divided into 12 equal pieces.

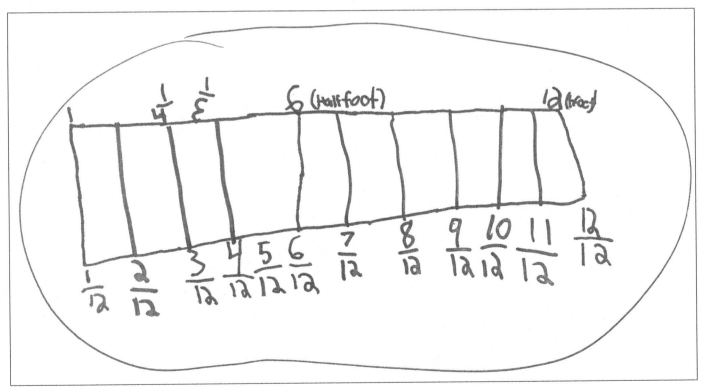

Figure 5: A sample showing 3/12 as half of 6/12.
However, note the placement of 1/12 at the 0 point instead of at the first line, and how there is no line for the 5/12. The students have their strip cut into 10 pieces instead of 12.

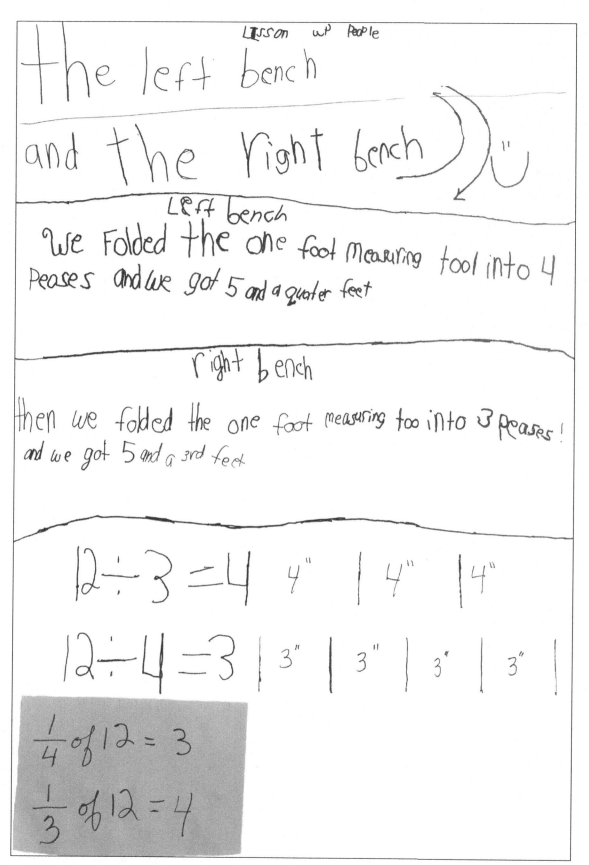

the left bench
Lesson w? People

and the right bench)ü

Left bench
We Folded the one foot measuring tool into 4
peases and we got 5 and a quater feet

right bench

then we folded the one foot measuring too into 3 peases!
and we got 5 and a 3rd feet

$12 \div 3 = 4$ 4" | 4" | 4"

$12 \div 4 = 3$ | 3" | 3" | 3" | 3" |

$\frac{1}{4}$ of 12 = 3

$\frac{1}{3}$ of 12 = 4

Figure 6: A sample showing the relationship between 1/4 of 12 = 3 and 1/3 of 12 = 4.

Once students have finished determining the length of one of the benches, they will need to do the other. This task provides an opportunity to consider other relationships. For example, if they find one of the benches is 63 inches and realize that is 5 $\frac{1}{4}$ feet, they will need to figure out the length of the other strip. If they use the 1/4 and decompose the 3 inches into 3 smaller equal pieces, they will see that the other bench is just one inch longer. Now they will need to figure out what fractional part of the foot 4 inches is. The minilesson earlier in the day may help students consider the relationship between 12/4 = 3 and 12/3 = 4. It may still be a leap for some to see that 12/3 means breaking the 12 into 3 equal parts, and thus 4 inches out of the 12 inches equals 1/3.

Some students may note that there is only a 1-inch difference between the two lengths. You might ask these children to consider what fraction of a foot an inch is. Support them to remember how many inches there are in a foot and ask if 12 means there are 12 equal parts. Remind them of the division: 1 divided by 12 = 1/12. The fraction bar means division. This discussion can lead children to consider that 3 inches can be represented as 3 x 1/12 of a foot, which also equals 3/12.

Other students may start with the 64-inch strip first. Measuring this length with the strip will produce 5 feet and a familiar a dilemma. The piece left is shorter than the strip. How to measure it? Folding a strip into three equal pieces is difficult, but if students lay the strip down next to the remaining section to be measured and mark the end of the bench piece they will have the first third. If they fold on the line, and fold again at the end of the first folded strip, they get 3 equal pieces. (See Figure 7.) Support students to see this as 1/3—1 divided by 3. So 12 inches divided by 3 is 4 inches. Now they have a nice equivalence: 1/3 = 4/12.

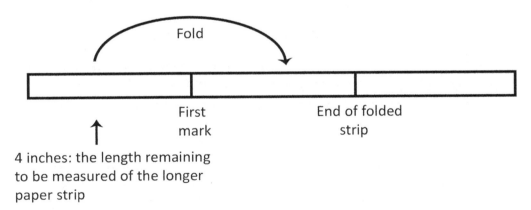

Figure 7. The foot-long strip being folded into thirds.

Carol (teacher): I've been watching what you two are doing and it looks like such an interesting strategy. Can I sit and confer with you? *(The students are working on the 64-inch length.)*

Antonio: Sure.

Liza: We are trying to figure out how long the last piece of board will be, but we can't fold our paper to get it right.

Carol: I can see that you used that efficient folding strategy we talked about in the math congress yesterday. So it isn't working with this strip? Why do you think it's harder with this one?

Antonio: When we fold the half into half it isn't long enough to quite reach the end of this piece. You know, the leftover part of 12 inches.

Liza: Yeah, it needs to be a different length. But are there more fractions than 1/2 and 1/4?

Carol: What do you think Antonio? Are there more fractions? *(Both students are silent.)* Hmm. Let's think about what we know about fractions. Why do we use that kind of notation with the bar? Which operation in math did the bar represent?

Antonio: Oh, wait! I know this! I just can't remember it...

Carol: *(After some wait time)* Can you help, Liza?

Liza: I think it's dividing? We have 12 inches, right? So maybe we can measure the part that is left over and see how many pieces we get.

Antonio: I know it's going to be bigger than 1/4 because 1/4 was too small. Maybe if we divide the strip into 3 equal pieces instead of 4. That would make it a little longer I think.

Carol: You both agree then that you are dividing the 12 inches into a number of parts? Before, you divided it into 4 equal pieces and you found out that each piece was 3 inches out of 12 inches and that was 1/4. This reminds me of our minilesson and all of the relationships we talked about earlier. If 12/4 was 3, what would 12/3 be? Is there a relationship?

Liza: I think so...

Author's notes

Note how Carol listens first before she sits down. She then explains what she thinks the pair is doing and asks for clarification. Once she is sure of their strategy she will be able to better support them. The intent is not to lead them to a strategy she may know or to an answer, but to support them as young mathematicians.

Notice how Carol encourages the two students to help each other.

Antonio has hit upon a big idea: the bigger the denominator the smaller the piece. When students are introduced to fractions in a division context they quickly come to realize that the bigger the divisor the smaller the quotient. They don't develop the misconception we often see when children are introduced to fractions using a part/parts model. (They often assume that 1/4, for example, is bigger than 1/3 because 4 parts must be bigger than 3 parts.)

Carol: Try thinking about how many inches that might be. Can you think of a notation with a bar that represents what you're doing? I'm going to go over and confer with Mya's group, but I will check back with you later to see what kind of fabulous strategy you invent together, ok?	*Carol encourages the pair to consider the relationships discussed in the minilesson: 4 x 3 = 3 x 4 and 12/4 = 3, so 12/3 = 4. These are big ideas for these young mathematicians and Carol leaves them to allow them sufficient think time to work through their thinking.*

As students begin to reach conclusions about the lengths of the two new benches, ask them to prepare posters presenting their findings for a gallery walk and congress on Day Four. Explain that mathematicians often want to share their findings with each other, and that when they do they are careful to choose the most important ideas to share. As students prepare their work on poster paper, they should not copy or explain every step they took. Instead, encourage students to record how their thinking changed, the interesting connections they noticed, and the arguments they used to convince each other that their answers were correct. How did they convert from inches to fractional sections of feet? Did they notice any relationships between the two lengths? What did they notice along the way that might have made their work easier?

Reflections on the Day

Today your students had several opportunities to examine how the relationships between multiplication and division and the commutative property can be helpful. In the minilesson they explored how 3x8 = 8x3, and how 24/8 = 3 and thus 24/3 = 8. Later, as they worked to determine the lengths of the two additional benches, they discovered it was helpful to remember the commutative property and to use 3x4 = 4x3. If 1/4 of 12 is 3, then 1/3 of 12 is 4. Some children may also have noted that 1/2 of 1/2 produced 1/4. They may have constructed the idea that, when halving a fraction, one can just keep the denominator the same and halve the numerator: 1/2 of 6/12 is 3/12. Still others may have constructed the idea that smaller fractions lengths can be combined when they noted that 3/12 = 3 x 1/12. All of these discoveries are big ideas for young mathematicians. Celebrate their noticings and ask the community to justify their thinking. Remember to reflect on what you see each day, on the big ideas being constructed as children work and on the strategies you see them using. Document the growth you see on the landscape. If you are using the New Perspectives assessment app, take a short video clip and a picture of children's work and add it to the landscape.

DAY FOUR

COMPARING 1/3 AND 1/4

Materials Needed

Sticky notes (two or three per student)

Students' work from Day Three

Pencils

Today begins with students adding finishing touches to posters from Day Three. Next, students take a gallery walk during which they notice and wonder about other students' work and compare it to their own. After the gallery walk, a congress is held to discuss a few of the emerging ideas about fractions more deeply. The congress ends with a minilesson. Students end with a string of related problems once again designed to support understanding of the relationship between multiplication and division.

Day Four Outline

Facilitating the Gallery Walk

❖ Confer with children as they put finishing touches to their posters, asking them to consider the most important things they want to tell their audience about their discoveries. Note and encourage justifications of big ideas and strategies described in the overview and depicted on the landscape.

❖ Conduct a gallery walk to allow students time to reflect and comment on each other's posters.

Facilitating the Math Congress

❖ Convene students at the meeting area to discuss a few important ideas that have surfaced in their work.

Minilesson: A String of Related Problems

❖ Work on a string of related problems designed to encourage use of the relationship between multiplication and division and equivalence of different representations.

Facilitating the Gallery Walk

Ask students to return to the posters they began on Day Three, adding any finishing touches they desire. As they work, move around and confer, asking them to consider the most important things they want to tell their audience and how they will convince them. For example, have some students noticed that the commutative property of multiplication (3x4 = 4x3) is at work here? The ways students see the division in these tasks matters, too. 12/4 = 3 could be seen as partitive division if students see it as making 4 equal groups resulting in lengths that are each 3 inches long. If students say that a 3-inch piece fits into the 12 inches 4 times, they are using quotative division. This is represented as 12/3 = 4. The terms partitive and quotative are not important for children to know. But how you represent and discuss their thinking does matter as you'll want to help children talk about the relationship between 12/4 = 3 and 12/3 = 4 and how these two divisions are related to 4x3 = 3x4. As they work on their posters, remind students that it is not necessary to write about everything they did, but instead to concentrate on convincing their audience about the important things they discovered and want to share and justify.

While the main purpose of the gallery walk is to publish viable arguments and defend them, a secondary purpose is to provide students with time for refinement of their thinking. As you move around conferring and helping your students to get ready for the gallery walk, look for ways to take their understanding to a deeper level or to justify generalizations of big ideas that emerged.

Once students have posted their work, remind them that gallery walks should be quiet times so that all mathematicians can read and think before commenting. This time should be taken seriously. During the gallery walk it's important for you to look for big ideas and strategies from the landscape. This is also the time to plan which pieces of work you will select for the congress.

Facilitating the Math Congress

Review the posters and choose a few that you can use for a discussion that will deepen understanding and support growth along the landscape of learning described in the overview. You'll want to pick pieces of work that will foster discussion on the big ideas that emerged during this investigation. For example, if a pair noted the commutative relationship (3x4 = 4x3) and how one bench was $5\frac{1}{3}$ feet while the other was $5\frac{1}{4}$ feet, use their work to focus a discussion on the relationships.

Perhaps there is a piece of work where a pair has explored 3/12 = 1/4 and 4/12 = 1/3. This would allow a deepening discussion of the relationships in the first piece as both approaches are related to the commutative relationship of 3x4 = 4x3. Do they see the underlying commutative property in the following: 1/4 of 12 equals 3; and 1/3 of 12 equals 4? Others may have noted that 1/4 is half of 1/2 and that 3/12 is half of 6/12. Work like this might provide for reflection on how fractions can be halved in two ways: keeping numerators the same but doubling the denominator (from 1/2 to 1/4); or by keeping the denominator the same and halving the numerator (6/12 to 3/12). Look at students' work with an eye to the big ideas and strategies on the landscape and you will see the potential for many rich discussions.

Inside One Classroom: A Portion of the Math Congress

Carol (the teacher): Jamal and Isabella, would you start us off? Come share with us what you discovered. I saw you doing some folding and comparing while you were working. You also got stuck once or twice. I think some of us were also stuck in some places. Maybe you can tell us how you worked through this juicy problem.

Jamal: For the first one we were able to figure it out fast. We folded the foot in half like in the first bench and then we just folded that one in half again. And we got 1/4 because then there were 4 parts of the whole thing. So the bench needs to be 5 $\frac{1}{4}$ feet. We figured out that the piece was 3 inches long because 12 divided by 4 is 3.

Isabella: Yeah, we thought the next one would be easy too. But not so much.

Carol: *(turning to the whole class)* Thumbs up: did anyone else find it easy by folding the 1/2 into 1/2 again? What about the second strip? It seems that many of the other mathematicians in our classroom had the same experience.

Isabella: So that didn't work with the other piece. But we knew that 1/4 is 3 inches because 12 divided by 4 is 3. I thought that would help us but I wasn't exactly sure how so I thought and thought, and Jamal did, too.

Jamal: Then we saw that if 12 divided by 4 is 3 that means that 4 x 3 = 12. And then 3 x 4 = 12 because you can just switch them around. That made us think that the other bench had to be 5 $\frac{1}{3}$ feet long. The 1/3 piece is 4 inches long because 12/3 = 4.

Carol: So are you saying that what you know about multiplication can even help you with division? You two used that special relationship in multiplication that switches factors around. Damian and Isa…. Come share your work next. I think it may be connected to what Jamal and Isabella are talking about. Let's see.

Damian: We noticed that the 1/4 was also 3/12 because a 3" piece fits into 12" four times.

Isa: And then we realized that a 4" piece fits into the foot 3 times, so that gave us 4/12.

Jamal: Yup. It is connected! 3 x 4 = 4 x 3.

Carol: Turn and talk to an elbow partner. Do you agree with Jamal and Isa? Do you see a relationship here?

Author's notes

Carol asks Jamal and Isabella to share first. They were challenged by how to make thirds, but they worked through their struggle with tenacity. One of the Standards of Mathematical Practice is "solves problems with tenacity and perseverance." By commenting on the students' struggle and asking them to share, Carol illuminates what it means to do mathematics—she is emphasizing the process.

The commutative property is now at the heart of the discussion.

Notice when Carol uses pair talk. She uses it strategically when she wants to promote reflection on a big idea. Children need time to make sense of ideas for themselves.

Minilesson: A String of Related Problems

This string starts with learners' understanding of the relationship between division and multiplication. Use the open number line to represent students' thinking and use both the fraction notation (the bar) and the division sign (÷) to represent the division. Using both notations interchangeably will support your students to see them both as division. As in previous minilessons, the same numerals are used in sets to focus reflection on the related operations of multiplication and division. Depending on how children describe their thinking, representations on the open number line will likely foster further reflections on the two types of division: partitive division (the number of groups is known and you are trying to find the number in each group) and quotative division (you know the number in each group and you are trying to find the number of groups). If these relationships do not come up naturally as children share their strategies, the last two problems in the string (word problems) will ensure they emerge.

The String:

3 x 4

4 x 3

12 ÷ 3

12 ÷ 4

12/3

12/4

1/4 of 12

1/3 of 12

12 pencils for 3 groups, how many does each group get?

12 pencils with 4 in each group, how many groups?

Reflections on the Day

Today began with a gallery walk. Students were able to show different ways to produce the exact measurements of the boards needed for the benches on the sides of the meeting area. Students used the relationship between multiplication and division to explain their thinking and solutions. Some students explored the relationship between partitive and quotative division, though without naming them, while others may be just starting to discern that there are different ways to divide. In the minilesson your mathematicians looked at the commutative property of multiplication and its relationship to division. Today you had a chance to look at the students' work and get a better idea of where each student is travelling on the landscape of learning. If you are interested in tracking your students' journeys digitally, check out www.NewPerspectivesonAssessment.com.

DAY FIVE

WHAT'S THE FRACTION? WHAT'S THE WHOLE?

Materials Needed

1-foot rulers with 1/2- and 1/4-inch hash marks (one per pair of students)

Pencils

Several sheets of copy or drawing paper

Blank Chart Paper for posters (sticky note style is best as it makes taping on the walls unnecessary)

Markers

Today begins with a minilesson employing the double number line to explore a string of related problems. The string is designed to support discussion on several ideas: 1) fractions are relations—the size or amount of the whole matters; 2) fractions are numbers between 0 and 1; and 3) to name a fraction we need to know what the whole is. A subsequent investigation occurs on what the lines between the inches on a ruler might represent.

Day Five Outline

Minilesson: A string of related problems

❖ Students explore points on a 1-foot line as fractions between 0 and 1 and also as a ratio of number of inches to the whole of 12 inches. The relationships are represented on a double number line.

Developing the Context

❖ Working in pairs, students investigate the marks between inches as fractions of an inch and as fractions of a foot, determining what to name the fraction and what the whole is.

Supporting the Investigation

❖ As students work, move around and confer. Support students to notice that 1/2 of an inch is much smaller than 1/2 of a foot and to explain why 1/2 of an inch can also be seen as 1/24 of a foot. Determining what the whole is and how many parts it has matters!

Minilesson: A string of related problems

Display a 1-foot piece of string or masking tape on a board, or draw a 1-foot line on the white board. Alternately, you can project a line from your computer onto a smart board, but make sure if you do this that the projected line that appears on the smart board is exactly 1 foot. Tell students that you measured the length carefully before you cut it and that it is exactly one foot long. Use a foot ruler to show them. Mark the beginning point with a zero and the endpoint with a 1, explaining that the 1 represents 1 foot. Place these numbers just slightly above the string as shown below:

0   1
_____

As you invite discussion on each problem in the string you will be building a double number line model with fractional parts of the foot written above the line and the number of inches written below the line. For each fraction or amount of inches, ask students to approximate where the number should be marked and have them justify their reasoning. The purpose of the double number line is to allow students to flexibly move back and forth from whole numbers to fractions—to see fractions as a number between 0 and 1 and simultaneously as a ratio of parts to parts. For example, after the first two problems you will likely have a representation similar to the one shown below:

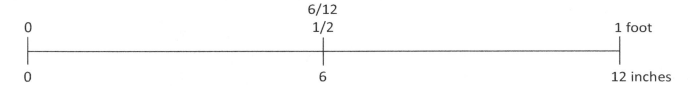

The String:
Where is 1/2 of the whole foot?
How many inches is 1/2 of 12?
Where is 1/4 of the whole foot?
How many inches is 1/4 of 12?
Where is 1/8 of the whole foot?
How many inches is 1/8 of 12?
Where is 2/4 of the whole foot?
How many inches is 2/4 of 12?
Where is 3/4 of the whole foot?
How many inches is 3/4 of 12?
Where is 1/3 of the whole foot?
How many inches is 1/3 of 12?
Where is 2/3 of the whole foot?
How many inches is 2/3 of 12?

Behind the Numbers

When fractions are thought of as numbers, a point on a number line between 0 and 1, the whole is common: it is 1. In this minilesson there are two common wholes: 12 inches and 1 foot. The string is designed to support discussion on several ideas: 1) fractions are relations—the size or amount of the whole matters; 2) fractions are numbers between 0 and 1; and 3) to name a fraction we need to know what the whole is. This string also allows for the generating of another big idea: if you have a common whole, you can compare two numbers. For example, you can compare 1/4 to 1/2 because the numerators are the same, or 1/4 to 2/4 because the denominators are the same. As you move through the string, invite students to consider relationships. For example, 1/4 is 1/2 of 1/2. 1/8 is 1/2 of 1/4. 2/4 can be thought of as 2 x 1/4 and 2/3 can be thought of as 2 x 1/3. As students consider where to place 1/3 you might ask them to consider how it relates to 1/4. Will it be larger or smaller? They may remember their discussions earlier in the week regarding 1/3 of 12 equaling 4, and 1/4 of 12 equaling 3. This discussion may provide an opportunity to revisit the connection to the commutative property: 3 x 4 = 4 x 3.

Inside One Classroom: A Portion of the Minilesson

Carol (the teacher): *(beginning discussion on the second problem)* So when you thought of the first problem you all said we should think of the line folded or cut in half, 1 ÷ 2. So I drew it here like you said, halfway between 0 and 1. So now let me write a second problem. How many inches is 1/2 of 12 inches? Thumbs up when you have an idea. *(She provides wait time until most students have a thumb up.)* Now turn and talk to a friend about where 1/2 of the foot is on the line and how many inches you think that is. *(She provides time for discussion.)* Did anyone have a partner who had an interesting idea?

Mya: Yes, Sasha says that 1/2 of the foot is in the middle because it's divided into 2 even parts and 6 is also in the middle of 12, because 6 + 6 = 12.

John: Yeah, me and Ben think the same thing.

Lisa: Isabella and Jamal and I think so, too.

Carol: So I'll write 12 inches right here, right under the 1 foot, because we can think of the measurements either in feet or inches. 6 inches is in the middle, too? Is it right underneath the 1/2? Then could I also write 6/12 of a foot on the top above the 1/2?

Lots of voices: Yes!

Author's notes

Carol writes one problem at a time and represents children's responses using a double number line: fractions of feet are represented on the top of the line, and the inches are represented underneath the line. This provides a visible ratio.

Notice how Carol keeps the flow of the dialogue going kid-to-kid, interspersed with reflection time as kids talk to one another.

Carol: Share your idea, Liam.

Liam: 6 inches is 1/2 of 12 because 12 divided by 2 is 6; so it's 6 inches.

Carol: Any other ideas? Arturo? No, you agree? Alright, let's go to the next problem then. Where is 1/4 of the whole foot? Thumbs up when you are ready to discuss this. *(Carol provides think time.)* Ok, talk to someone near you and tell them what you think. Be sure to be a good partner and listen carefully. *(Carol listens in with a group near her.)* Did anyone's partner have an idea that interested them?

Juanita: Hayden says that it should be halfway between the beginning, where the 0 is, and the 1/2 mark, because when we were folding papers the other day when we were measuring for the benches, we folded a half in half and we got 1/4.

Hayden: Like half of a half is a quarter or a fourth.

Carol: I am going to go half way between the left end of the line and the 1/2 mark to show 1/4. Is that accurate for your thinking, Hayden? *(Carol marks the 1/4 above the line halfway between 0 and 1/2.)*

Hayden: Yup.

Paulette: Oh, so that makes sense. If you take a half and you fold it you have twice as many parts. 2 doubled is 4.

Carol: That's an interesting idea, Paulette. Let's see if there are any problems in our string as we continue that make you think of that again. You let me know if you see any, please.

Paulette: I think there probably will be. I'll be on the lookout.

Carol: How many inches is 1/4 of 12 inches? Thumbs when you are ready. *(Carol provides think time and then resumes.)* What do you think, Alton?

Alton: I think it's 3 because Hayden said half of a half is a quarter so half of 6 is 3.

Carol: So on the double number line if I jump half of the half of a foot that is 1/4? On the bottom, then, half of 6 inches is 3 inches. Is that what you're thinking it looks like, Alton?

Alton: Yes.

Carol: So can I also write 3/12 up here above the 1/4? These fractions are equal? Wow. So here is a challenge then. Where is 1/8 of one foot? Turn and talk and let me know when you

Carol heard Liam discussing division earlier and calls on him to bring that perspective into the conversation.

By asking if anyone had an interesting partner Carol implies that her expectations are that everyone will be a good partner: listening carefully; and making sure the pair talk is "accountable talk."

Note how Carol has the fractions on the top of the line and whole numbers (the inches) on the bottom. This supports kids to use whole numbers to set up a ratio of part/parts when making fractions.

Paulette has noticed that the denominator has doubled but the fraction has been halved. This is a big idea on the landscape. By inviting Paulette to look for it happening again, Carol fosters looking for structure and regularity—one of the Standards of Mathematical Practice.

Note how the fractions are kept on top. 3/12 = 1/4.

have an idea. *(She provides wait time, then resumes discussion.)* Who wants to share an idea?

Paulette: Wait! Wait!

Carol: What is it, Paulette?

Paulette: This is one of those questions! Remember I'm on the lookout for questions about doubling a number on the bottom to make the fraction half. The 8 is a double. I knew there would be one!

Carol: Hmmm. What do you think, mathematicians, is this a question we can solve using Paulette's strategy? Before, Paulette said if you double the divisor you get twice as many pieces. Would 1/2 of 1/4 be 1/8? Discuss with a friend and be ready to share your opinion. *(Carol listens in on a few discussions to gauge the level of understanding.)* Friends, I think we have had some great discussions going on here. I even heard groups discussing with other groups. Let's hear some of those ideas.

Note how Carol introduces proper math terminology naturally. This rephrasing is not exactly what Paulette said earlier but it is close enough for everyone to understand a more formal version of Paulette's idea.

Juan: Angel was my partner. We think it works if you double the 4, because double 4 is 8 so then you get 1/8, but you don't have 4 pieces, you have 8 pieces... so it is half as much. Paulette is right!

Carol: So to capture your thinking, you are saying that 1/8 goes halfway between the beginning of the line and 1/4? *(Carol marks and labels the line.)* How many inches is 1/8 of 12?

Juan: It's half of 3. That's... it's more than 1 because 1 and 1 would only be 2.

Angel: It's $1\frac{1}{2}$. Like... $1.50 + $1.50 = $3.

Note how the children make sense of things in their own ways. Angel uses money as a tool.

Carol: Wow! So $1\frac{1}{2}$ inches is 1/8 of the 12 inches? So can I write "$1\frac{1}{2}$ over 12" above the 1/8, because before for 1/4 it was 3/12? That's interesting, isn't it? If we keep the denominator the same but halve the numerator is that half as much as well? Paulette what do you think? This is different than your strategy, but would this work, too?

Carol puts forth something else from the landscape for consideration: if denominators are the same, one could just halve a numerator. Note, however, that she doesn't tell them that it works. She asks if they think it will.

Developing the Context

Keep the work you did in the minilesson on the board so that students can refer to it as they work. Explain to the students that you have some new rulers to pass out. Show them how there are some little marks in between each of the inch marks on these and explain that you wondered what they might be for. You started to think about why the marks were between each of the inch numbers all the way up to 12 inches. You were wondering what the marks might represent. Might the marks represent more than one thing? Once students being pondering about the marks, send them off to investigate with a partner.

Supporting the Investigation

As students work, move around and listen to their conversations and justifications. Notice if students just count the ticks, for example noting 3 ticks and erroneously calling each tick a third. Others may realize that 3 ticks are dividing the space (the inch) into 4 equal smaller lengths, effectively making fourths. As you confer you can also support children to notice that each full inch is also 4/4 of an inch (as well as 2/2), and that the 1/2 is also 2/4 of an inch.

A strategy you might notice also is the use of halving: halving the inch produces halves; halving the halves produces fourths. This is the strategy that Paulette (in the minilesson dialogue box) has begun to notice. This is a big idea on the landscape: if numerators are kept the same, doubling the denominator halves the fraction.

Note whether students think of the third tick as 3 x 1/4. If not, you may choose to support this by asking how many sections the inch has been broken up into.

Some children may also talk about how the half mark between the 1 and the 2 can also be thought of as 3 halves (3/2). Don't be afraid to challenge students by asking how many half inches are in the whole ruler! Note how they respond. Some students may just count, but others may even use a little proportional reasoning! If there are 2 halves in each inch, then there must be 24 half-inches on the ruler. Thus, each 1/2 of an inch is also 1/24 of a foot! Don't be afraid to write this statement down and ask students whether it is a true or not. Let your children surprise you. This is a much richer investigation than you might think!

As students finish, ask them to prepare a poster to share the meanings they found for the marks and important things they have noticed as they worked. These posters will be used on Day Six in a gallery walk and math congress.

Reflections on the Day

Math workshop began today with a unique minilesson; a series of questions designed to lead students to think about how the size of the whole matters when determining what to call a fractional part. The number of equal parts in the whole matters. The minilesson also supported the development of the double number line as a representational model. Over time this model will become a powerful tool to think with as children explore addition and subtraction of fractions in later years. Fractions are numbers and they are also relations. The whole matters. For example, 1/8 can actually be more than 1/4 if we are talking about 1/8 of a foot versus 1/4 of an inch. Once this big idea is constructed, students come to understand that a common whole is needed to compare fractions. In the gallery walk and congress on Day Six you will be able to discuss these big ideas in greater depth.

Experiences such as this investigation and discussion of the big ideas they help construct are critical if students are to understand fractions deeply. Today you built a strong foundation to address and/or help avoid common misconceptions. Children often think that when comparing unit fractions, greater denominators mean greater values, when in fact the opposite is true. 1/8 is not more than 1/7; it is less! Today your students likely also realized that even whole units can be represented as fractions—4/4 = 1; 8/4 = 2. They may even have considered how 1/2 of an inch = 1/24 of a foot (or 1/24 of 12 inches)! Don't forget to document what you saw developing today. It might be helpful to take some pictures of the work at the end of the day and make some anecdotal notes. This is truly evidence-based practice.

DAY SIX

CONSIDERING
FRACTIONAL LENGTHS

Materials Needed

1-foot rulers with 1/2- and 1/4-inch hash marks (one per pair of students)

Pencils and Markers

Sticky notes

Several sheets of copy or drawing paper

Blank Chart Paper for posters (sticky note style is best as it makes taping on the walls unnecessary)

Today begins with a minilesson employing the use of the double number line to explore a string of related problems. The string, like the one on Day Five, is designed to support discussion on several ideas: 1) fractions are relations—the size or amount of the whole matters; 2) fractions are numbers between 0 and 1; and 3) to name a fraction we need to know what the whole is. Time is given for students to finish up their posters and then a gallery walk and congress focus on the questions from Day Five: what do the lines between the inches on a ruler represent; what is the fraction; and what is the whole that it refers to?

Day Six Outline

Minilesson: A string of related problems

❖ Students explore points on a line as fractions between 0 and 1 and also as the ratio of a number of inches to a whole of 18 inches. The relationships are represented on a double number line.

Preparing for Math Congress

❖ Students add finishing touches to their posters from Day Five and then engage in a gallery walk.

Facilitating the Math Congress

❖ Support students to notice that 1/2 of an inch is much smaller than 1/2 of a foot and to explain why. 1/2 of an inch can also be seen as 1/24 of a foot. Determining what the whole is and how many parts it has matters!

Minilesson: A string of related problems

The minilesson today is very similar to the minilesson on Day Five, except that the length of the line is now 18 inches. This is purposeful to engage students in considering again how the whole matters. The "1" today now refers to 1 length of 18 inches, not 12 inches. As on Day Five you can use a piece of string, a strip of masking tape, or just draw a line. But, measure carefully to ensure the length is exactly 18 inches. If you project from your computer onto a smart board, make sure that the projected image that appears on the smart board is exactly 18 inches. Before you start, explain to your students that the minilesson is very similar to the one on Day Five with one important difference: today the length is 18 inches. Measure with a ruler or yardstick to show them. Mark the beginning point with a 0 and the endpoint with a 1, explaining that this time it is 1 piece that is 18 inches, not 1 foot. As you did before, place these numbers just slightly above the string as shown below:

0   1

As you invite discussion on each problem in the string you will be building a double number line model again with fractional parts of the length written above the line and the number of inches written below the line. For each fraction or amount of inches, ask students to approximate where the number should be marked and have them justify their reasoning. Remember that the purpose of the double number line is to allow students to flexibly move back and forth from whole numbers to fractions—to see fractions as a number between 0 and 1 and simultaneously as a ratio of parts to parts. For example, after the first two problems you will likely have a representation similar to the one shown below:

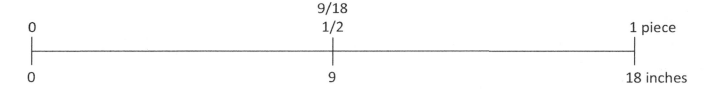

The String:

Where is 1/2 of the length?
How many inches is the 1/2 mark?
Where is 1/3 of the length?
How many inches is 1/6 of the length?
What is 1/6 of 18?
How many inches in 2/3 of the length?
How many inches in 2/6 of the length?
How many inches in 3/6 of the length?

Preparing for the Math Congress

If students need more time to put finishing touches to their posters, provide it. As they work, students will likely reflect more deeply on many of the big ideas you'll want to focus on in the congress. This time also provides you with an opportunity to push students' thinking again, challenging them to justify their arguments in ways that will convince their peers. As they finish, have students display their posters around the classroom for other groups to view in the gallery walk. Give students only a few sticky notes so that they have to think carefully about where they will place them. Have students walk around and read a few of the posters silently for 5-10 minutes, making sure that every poster gets read by a least a few children and that every poster gets at least a few sticky notes.

After the gallery walk, invite the groups to return to their posters to see what comments were left. Allow students a few minutes to think about this feedback and any new ideas they now have. Provide time for a short discussion with partners before convening the whole class in the meeting area.

Teacher Note

If most students are in the early stages of poster work, it can sometimes seem premature to hold a congress. You can start by providing everyone with more work time as is suggested here, but alternately you can also hold a gallery walk on students' early work. Explain that no one is finished and that students are not commenting on final work, but rather on other groups' starting ideas. A gallery walk with this structure can help cross-pollinate ideas between partnerships and re-energize groups to return to work on their posters before a math congress occurs.

Facilitating the Math Congress

As you consider a plan for the congress, note the strategies used and look for evidence of big ideas that will help you structure the discussion. Review the landscape in the Overview and consider how a congress could benefit each child. The congress is not a place to discuss one intended outcome for all; it is a place for a discussion that can support development of all of your students, often in different ways.

If several students just counted the ticks between inches, erroneously calling each tick a third, there may be disagreement among groups as to whether the ticks represent thirds or fourths. If this is the case, you might want to start the congress with this disagreement. Using disagreements as a focus engenders disequilibrium and this can be a powerful incentive for developing argumentation and eventual cognitive reordering. Ask students to present both sides and get everyone involved. It is important to provide time for students to consider this important issue: it is the length (the inch) that is being cut up into equal smaller lengths to make fractional pieces; the ticks represent boundaries rather than pieces of the length. If you start your congress this way, note whether any students think of the space marked by the third tick as 3 x 1/4. Three sections of fourths equal 3/4. If not, support them to do so where appropriate. This is also a nice place to focus some discussion on whether the inch could also be considered 4/4, and the two inches 8/4, etc.

A strategy you might also have noticed is the use of halving: halving the inch produces halves; halving the halves produces fourths. If you choose a pair to share this strategy you can use the moment to support a generalization: if numerators are kept the same, doubling the denominator halves the fraction. Ask students to consider if this will always happen and to explain why.

Many students may have just counted sections and labeled them, but you may have noticed others using a little proportional reasoning—if there are 2 halves in each inch, then there must be 24 half-inches on the ruler. Thus, each 1/2 of an inch is also 1/24 of a foot! This could be a very nice piece to use last to really encourage your students to consider how the whole matters. You can refer back to the minilesson today where 9 was the halfway point of 18, while the halfway point of the foot was 6 inches since the whole was 12 inches.

Inside One Classroom: A Portion of the Math Congress	
Carol (the teacher): So we seem to have a bit of a disagreement—at least it seemed that way to me as I read your posters. Several of you decided that each tick was a third, and several of you said the ticks represented fourths. Which is it, thirds or fourths? Let's start our congress by discussing this. Yolanda and Sean, would you share why you called them thirds, and then we'll hear from Isabella and Mya about why they called them fourths.	
Yolanda: There are 3 ticks in each inch, so each tick is 1 out of 3 ticks.	*Author's notes*
Sean: Yeah, and 1 out of 3 parts is 1/3.	*Carol starts the congress with two discrepant ideas. By doing this she pushes her students to consider mathematical arguments.*
Carol: How many people agree with Yolanda and Sean, that there are 3 ticks and 1 out of 3 is 1/3? *(Five or six hands go up.)* Ok, now let's hear from Isabella and Mya about why they called them fourths.	
Isabella: We thought of the inch like a tiny strip and we know from our work the other day that if we folded the strip in half and then folded it in half again we would get fourths—4 equal pieces.	
Mya: I think it matters what we call the whole, like in our minilesson. If there were just 3 ticks on a page and they didn't mean anything...they were just ticks...1 out of 3 would be 1/3. Or like 3 balls, 1 out of 3 would be 1/3. But these ticks are measuring lengths, just like the inches and the feet. I think we have to think about the space in between the ticks, and there are 4 equal spaces.	*Mya's justification is a powerful one. The whole is not made up of ticks; it is made up of smaller equal lengths. Because the whole is the inch, it's distance that matters.*
Carol: Ok, find an elbow partner. Talk this over. What do you think, thirds or fourths? *(After sufficient pair talk time, Carol moves back to whole-group discussion.)* What did you decide? Yolanda?	

Yolanda: I changed my mind. I think Mya and Isabella are right. The ticks are fourths, so 1/4, 2/4, and 3/4. Hey, is the inch 4/4? *(Many puzzled faces at first, and murmurs.)*

Carol: Sean, you look puzzled. What are you thinking about what Yolanda said?

Sean: Are those numbers fractions?

Mya: Yes. 3/4 is 1/4 three times: 1/4 + 1/4 + 1/4.

Sean: But how could the inch be 4/4? The inch isn't a fraction. It's the whole thing!

Mya: I know, I'm not sure either. But I think, maybe yes. Because it is 1/4 four times: 1/4 + 1/4 + 1/4 + 1/4. That's 4 x 1/4. And that would make the whole inch. So maybe it is right.

Carol: Remember that in our minilesson last week we talked about how the bar was just another way to write division? What is 4 divided by 4?

Liam: Oh yeah....it is 1 inch. 4/4 means the whole thing.

Carol: So let me try to make a picture of this. I'll use a line like we did in the minilesson. *(Carol draws the following:)*

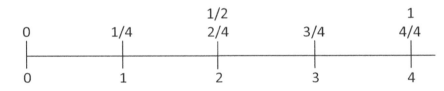

Julio: Yes. It works!

Lisa: Jamal and I think so, too.

Carol: So what about 2 inches? How many times would 1/4 inch fit into 2 inches? Jamal?

Jamal: There's 4 fourths in one inch, so there would be 8 in two inches.

Carol: So then I can write 8/4 for 2 inches?

Lots of voices: Yes!

Carol: Share your idea, Liam.

Liam: It's just division: 8 divided by 4 is 2!

Reflections on the Day

Math workshop began today with a minilesson similar to the one used on Day Five. But now the whole has changed, supporting children to continue to puzzle over the importance of the whole. The minilesson also continued the development of the double number line as a representational model. Over time this model will become a powerful tool to think with when, in later years, children explore addition and subtraction of fractions. Today your students likely also realized that even whole units can be represented as fractions—$4/4 = 1$ and $8/4 = 2$. In math workshop today, students had the opportunity to share and read each other's mathematical work and to explore how two fractions can be equal. For example, $2/4 = 1/2$; $9/18 = 1/2$; and $8/4 = 2$. A gallery walk and math congress provided opportunities for students to develop and reflect on even more equivalent expressions. Tomorrow, students will have an opportunity to design their own rulers.

DAY SEVEN

MAKING A RULER

Today begins with a minilesson designed to keep students thinking about the relationship between multiplication and division and to consider how, when thinking about fractions, the whole matters. Following the minilesson students make their own rulers, marking fractions of an inch. This investigation causes them to see how 1/2 of an inch is different than 1/2 of a foot—the whole matters--and how folding the strip can help them find the exact spots to mark.

Materials Needed

Strips of adding machine paper carefully measured to 12 inches (have several available strips for each group to allow for multiple drafts and revisions)

Pencils and Markers

Tape

Blank Chart Paper for posters (sticky note style is best as it makes taping on the walls unnecessary)

Day Seven Outline

Minilesson: A String of Related Problems
❖ Work on a string of related multiplication and division problems.

Developing the Context
❖ Explain to students that over the last week they have been using pre-made rulers, but you thought it would fun to make their own to take home. Because a ruler is a measuring tool, they will need to be precise about where they place numbers and to do this it might help to think about how the numbers are related.
❖ Working in pairs, students will make their own 12-inch rulers, including fractional pieces of inches.

Supporting the Investigation
❖ Move around and confer as students work, noting the strategies they use and supporting and challenging them to find the exact spots to mark using number relationships.

Minilesson: A string of related problems

The String:

12 ÷ 2

2 x 6

12 / 4

4 x 3

6 ÷ 2

6 / 1

3 / 3

3 / 1

1 ÷ 2

1/2 ÷ 2

1/4 x 2

Behind the Numbers

The numbers in this string have been carefully chosen to keep revisiting the relationship between multiplication and division. This idea sets the stage for thinking of fractions as division. As children divide a measurement unit into equal smaller sections they are using division: 1 inch divided by 4 = 1/4. They also experience a fraction as a portion of a unit: 1 out of 4 pieces, with 4 pieces as the whole: 4/4=1

Inside One Classroom: A Portion of the Minilesson

Carol (the teacher): Isabella, you just told me that the first two problems are related and then the next two problems are a pair, too. Tell us all more about this.

Isabella: If you divide 12 into 2 parts, you get 6, so 2 x 6 is 12. See, 6 + 6. That's 12.

Carol: You've just told us a very big idea! Can anyone tell us what they understood when Isabella was talking?

Jason: It's like the numbers are related to each other. When you use two of them then you have to have the last one left. So if you multiply 2 x 6 = 12 then 12 ÷ 2 = 6. You have all the numbers.

Chris: So multiplication is kind of the opposite of division. If you start with the 12 and then divide by 2, you get 6, and that's 2 equal parts: 6 + 6. And that's 2 x 6.

Carol: Let me try to represent all that mathematical thinking on the open number line. Is this a way we could picture it?

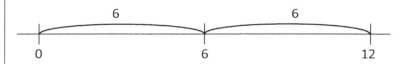

Isabella: Yes. You have a line of 12 and you divided it into 2 equal parts... and now you have 6 + 6, or 2 x 6 = 12.

Author's notes

The connections in this string have helped students articulate the reciprocal relationship between multiplication and division. Carol encourages them to elaborate on each other's ideas.

Carol: So could we also say that 1/2 of 12 is 6? Let's turn and talk about this with a partner.

Pat: Yes, because 6 is halfway.

Carol: Let me write it as a fraction. You said 6 was halfway to 12, so 6/12 = 1/2? Could we also say 6/1 = 6?

Pat: I think so. Maybe it depends on how you think about it. If you think about 6 being a part of 12, it is 6/12 and that is 1/2. But if you think about 6 being a number divided by 1, then the answer is just 6.

Isabella: Maybe it depends on what the whole is.

Pat: Yes. That's what I mean.

Carol: So is this right? *(She writes "6/1 = 6 and 6/12 = 1/2 and 6/6 = 1.")* Let's turn and talk again. *(After a sufficient amount of pair talk, Carol restarts the discussion.)*

Pat: Yeah. It just depends on how you want to think about it.

Now Carol "ups the ante" by asking students to consider division by 2 as taking 1/2 of a number.

Developing the Context

In this investigation students will be making their own rulers with a 12-inch piece of paper. However, they will not be able to refer to a pre-made ruler during this task. **This is an important constraint! Do NOT provide rulers as students will just copy them.** Instead, provide several 12-inch pieces of adding machine paper in order to allow for more than one draft. Some students will know that the paper measures 12 inches from working with the ruler during Day Five. If students do not realize it, tell them this information and suggest that they fold the paper to find other numbers. Ensure that before they go off to work, they all know that the strips have been measured to be exactly 12 inches. To develop the context, you might say something like the following:

> Over the last week the class has been using rulers, and it might be fun to make your own to take home. Because a ruler is a measuring tool, you will need to be very precise about where you place the numbers! It might help to think about how the numbers are related and to use folding to find the exact places to mark.

Remind the students of the experience they had on Day Five of the unit when they were looking at the rulers and the marks between the numbers. They had to think carefully about the size of the whole as an inch or as a foot. They realized that the size of the whole matters when comparing fractions; 1/4 of 12 inches is very different from 1/4 of an inch.

Have a discussion about what students might mark on their rulers. Should they mark only inches? How would they find the exact place for the other inches? For example, can they find 6 inches and know exactly where it is? Might folding help? How could they fold it? [If necessary, remind students of the minilesson and how 6 was half of 12.] Are there smart ways to find more of the numbers?

Should students also mark half inches, quarter inches, and maybe even more fractions? Let them decide with their partners how much detail they want to include. You can also guide the students to add detail if they are ready to make the leap to half and quarter inches as you confer during their work time.

Finally, before sending students off with their supplies, emphasize that there are more than enough strips of paper for them to revise as necessary. And precision matters!

Supporting the Investigation

Confer with children as they work, specifically looking at the strategies they use to mark the inches.

- ❖ Look for evidence of students' understanding of the distinction between 1/4 of the inch and 1/4 of the foot.
- ❖ Do they realize that 1/4 of a foot is 3 inches, that 1/3 of the foot is 4 inches, and that 2 inches is the halfway point between 0 and 4 inches?
- ❖ Do students estimate and check folds to partition the whole strip into three 4-inch pieces, or the 3-inch piece into three 1-inch pieces?
- ❖ Are students using their knowledge about dividing the foot into fractional parts?
- ❖ How do they make fractional pieces of the inch? Do they fold the inch in half, then fold it again to make fourths? Or, do they just estimate and draw lines? If the latter, remind them that this is a measuring tool and precision matters.
- ❖ You can differentiate by challenging some students to think about eighths and sixteenths of an inch.

As students finish, ask them to prepare a poster to convince others of their placements and markings of points and to justify the important things they have noticed along the way as they worked. They may want to tape their rulers to the posters. Because they will be using them again, it is a good idea to have them do so. These posters will be used on Day Eight in a gallery walk and congress.

Reflections on the Day

Today students worked on a string of related problems that most likely supported them as they worked to make their own rulers. Many students were likely able to explain the inverse relationship between the operations and to describe how the whole matters. In the minilesson they were also introduced to some new ideas: 6/6 equals 1, and 6/1 = 6.

In the investigation, students applied relationships they knew about division to find the precise place of numbers of inches, for example 12/2 = 6 and 12/4 = 3. They may have folded the strip to find 1/2 and 1/4 of a foot, and then continued to fold a 4-inch section into halves and halves again to find the other inches. They may even have gone on to find 1/8 and 1/16 of an inch! Others may have used more tedious strategies and struggled, for example trying to mark all the numbers by just estimating. That's okay. Tomorrow they will have a chance to hear about a variety of strategies that might have been more efficient. This is a community at work trying to solve a problem together, not individuals working alone to find a teacher's answer.

DAY EIGHT

CHECKING THE RULERS

Materials Needed

A piece of string or tape measuring 24 inches

Students' work from Day Seven

Student-made rulers

Classroom 12-inch rulers with 1/2- and 1/4-inch marks

A projector or document camera

Today begins with a string of related problems similar to the ones on Days Five and Six, but now dividing a 24-inch length of twine (or line) into fractional parts. They then have a gallery walk and math congress to discuss the strategies they used to make their rulers on Day Seven. Finally, students compare the rulers they made to standard rulers in the classroom, measure a variety of small objects in the classroom they think might be 1/4, 1/2, or 1 inch long, and make a line plot to represent the number of objects they found for each length.

Day Eight Outline

Minilesson: A string of related Problems

❖ Today's string is similar to Day Five's lesson. Instead of using 12 inches, the measure here is 24 inches. The string is purposely crafted to have students think about the whole when comparing fractions.

❖ When the string is completed, students will ponder the difference between the 12-inch string and the 24-inch string. They should be able to see that the lengths of the fractional pieces are double because the length of the whole is double.

The Gallery Walk

❖ Students participate in a gallery walk to share the strategies and final products they created during Day Seven's investigation.

❖ The purpose of the gallery walk is to allow students time to reflect and comment on each other's posters and the rulers they made.

Facilitating the Math Congress

❖ Convene students at the meeting area to discuss a few important ideas about their strategies for finding the exact location of different measurements. Compare student-made rulers with standard rulers in classroom and have students find objects in the room that measure 1/4, 1/2, or 1 inch. Compile their data and make a line plot.

Minilesson: A string of related problems

Display a 2-foot piece of string or masking tape on a board, or draw a 2-foot line on the white board. Alternately, you can project a line from your computer onto a smart board, but make sure if you do this that the projected line that appears on the smart board is exactly 2 feet, or 24 inches long. Tell students that you measured the length carefully before you cut (or drew) it and that it is exactly 2 feet long. Use a foot ruler to show them. Mark the beginning point with a zero and the endpoint with a 1, explaining that the 1 is for one length. Place these numbers just slightly above the string. Mark the inches and the feet underneath the string as shown below:

0   1 piece
_____

0   24 inches
                                                                                               2 feet

The String:
Where does 1/2 go on this line?
How many feet is that?
How many inches?
Where is 1/4 of the whole 24 inches?
Where is 1/8 of the whole 24 inches?
How many inches is 2/4 of 24 inches?
Where is 3/4 of the 24 inches?
Where is 1/3 of the whole length?
Where is 2/3 of the 24 inches?
Where is 3/3 of 24 inches?

As you discuss each problem in the string you will be employing a double number line model with fractions written above the line and the number of inches written below the line, just as you did on Days Five and Six. For each fraction or amount of inches, mark on the line where students estimate the numbers should be and have them explain their reasoning. The purpose of the double number line is to allow students to flexibly move back and forth from whole numbers to fractions—to see fractions as a number between 0 and 1 and simultaneously as a ratio of parts to parts. Students should also recognize equivalent fractions. For example, after the first two problems you will likely have a representation similar to the one shown below.

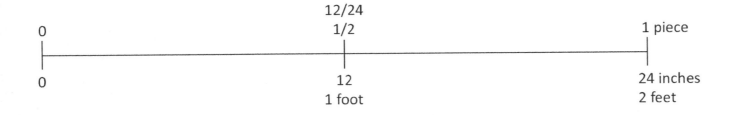

Facilitating the Gallery Walk

After the minilesson, ask students to return to the posters they began on Day Seven, adding any finishing touches they desire. As they work, move around and confer, asking them to consider the most important things they want to tell their audience about ways to mark their ruler. Remind students that it is not necessary to write about everything they did. Instead, ask them to concentrate on convincing their fellow mathematicians to look at the important discoveries they made as they worked to find the inches and the fractions of an inch. This is a good time to consider which posters to use for the math congress. If you like, you can take pictures of the student work you choose and then display the work during the congress by projecting it.

Facilitating the Math Congress

Review the posters from Day Seven and choose a few that you can use for a discussion that will deepen understanding and support growth along the landscape of learning described in the Overview. Think about how you might use the congress so that the discussion that occurs promotes new learning while confirming previously discovered big ideas. How did children approach this investigation? Did they fold the paper to divide it into halves, quarters, twelfths? How did they find the inches? Did they find 4 inches by finding 1/3 of the strip? Did any students realize that folding this 4-inch section in half and half again would produce the other inches? Are the parts of the ruler close to being the same size? If they wanted 12 equal parts, did they use 12 partitioning lines (giving them 13 equal parts)? If some did this, it demands lots of discussion. Use the context of measurement to help them understand that they need 12 equal lengths, not 12 ticks. Can they think in both fractional parts and inches?

After the math congress, give pairs of students a standard 12-inch ruler with 1/2 and 1/4 inches shown. Ask them to compare their homemade rulers to the real rulers, then have a quick group discussion about their noticings. How did their ideas and strategies for making the rulers affect the outcomes?

Lastly ask students to look around the room and try to find some objects that might be only 1/4, 1/2, of 1 inch thick, or long. Have them convene back in the meeting room to share their data. Compile the data onto a line plot that represents the number of objects they found for each of the three measurements. An example is shown on the following page.

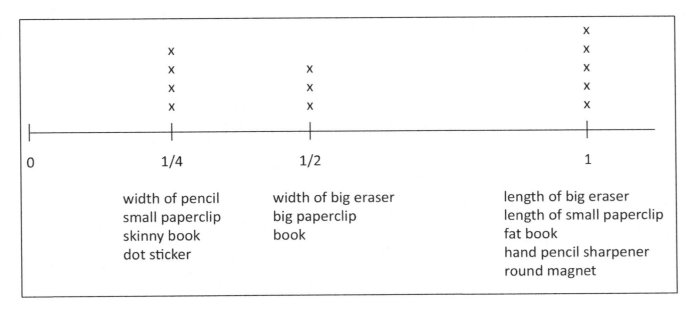

Figure 8. A sample line plot. Note how the distances are drawn to scale. The items are named here as examples, but listing them is not necessary.

Reflections on the Day

On Day Eight of this ten-day unit, students should show a much deeper understanding of how fractions represent division. With the minilesson, students had the opportunity to think about the size of the whole and how that is important in comparing fractions. The gallery walk and math congress were times for assessing what students have learned thus far over the course of the unit. Document their learning. You might consider using math journals and having students write about their strategies. Have them put their homemade rulers in their journals. You could also consider student portfolios—places where students can store the work they are most proud of. Formative assessment is best in the moment, and it is far more genuine this way!

DAY NINE

IN THE BAG OR
ON THE LINE?

Today begins with another string of related problems designed to stimulate discussion on equivalence. Afterwards students play a new game that engages them in comparing the relative size of different fractions and finding matches of equivalent fractions.

Day Eight Outline

Minilesson: A String of Related Problems

❖ Today's minilesson is a string of related problems that have been designed to generate a discussion on equivalent fractions. In order to illustrate students' thinking, you will again use a double number line with inches on the bottom and fractions on the top.

Playing a Game: Bag It or Hang It

❖ Convene students at the meeting area to show them how to play the game.
❖ Once they are clear on the directions, send them off in partners to play.

Supporting the Investigation

❖ As students play *Bag It or Hang It*, move around and support them as needed. Note the strategies they use to determine the placement of fractions on the line, and which pairs they easily find to be equivalent.

Minilesson: A string of related problems

Display a 2-foot piece of string or masking tape on a board, or draw a 2-foot line on the white board. Alternately, you can project a line from your computer onto a smart board, but make sure if you do this that the projected line that appears on the smart board is exactly 2 feet, or 24 inches long. Tell students that you measured the length carefully before you cut it and that it is exactly 2 feet long. Use a foot ruler to show them. Mark the beginning point with a zero and the midpoint with a 1, explaining that the 1 is for 1 length or 1 whole foot. Today you will all be using 1 foot as the whole. Mark the end of the line with the number 2, asking students why they think it is 2. Place these numbers on the top of the line, as you have been doing throughout the unit, with the corresponding inches under the line.

The String:

Where does 1/2 of a foot go?

How many inches is that?

Where does 1 $\frac{1}{2}$ feet go?

How many inches is that?

Where would 8/4 of a foot go?

How about 1/2 + 1/4 of a foot?

How about 3/4 of a foot?

How many inches is that?

Where would 12/12 of a foot go?

How many inches is that?

How about 4/4 of a foot?

How many inches is that?

How about 3 x 1/2 of a foot?

How about 3/2?

> **Teacher Note**
>
> At this point you may have some students who say 1/2 of 1 foot is also 1/4 of the 2 feet. Acknowledge that they are right. On the side (not on the line) you can write: 1/2 of 12 = 1/4 of 24 and celebrate that kids know this. **BUT, DON'T** label 1/4 above the 1/2 on the line as this is not correct. As numbers, 1/2 does not equal 1/4. Explain that today you are thinking of the whole as 1 foot and the fractions you will label on the line refer only to the foot as the whole. Then go on with the string.

As you discuss each problem in the string you will be employing a double number line model as you did on the prior days. Keep the fractions on the top of the line and the inches on the bottom. Keep reminding students that today the whole is 1 foot, even though you have labeled 2 feet on the line, too. At the end of the string you might encourage students to think about how 3 divided by 2 equals 1 $\frac{1}{2}$. As you listen to and observe students you may see students who have developed a strong sense of fractions as division and equivalence. Others may still be challenged. You may want to make a mental note of which students may need a little more discussion and find that group (or groups) for a conferral when you start the partner game, described below.

Developing the Context:

Gather students on the rug to explain the rules of a new game: *Bag It or Hang It?*

Begin making this game with manila folders, one for each partnership. On the inside of each folder staple a piece of string from one end to the other. (This length is usually around 17 inches, end to end, but don't write the inches. Just mark 0 on the left under the staple and 1 on the right under the staple.) For each folder, assemble a plastic bag with paper clips and the cards from Appendix B.

Teacher Tip

The bags can be stapled to the folders and the name of the game can be written on the folder's tab. This way all playing pieces are organized and attached to the playing board, and the tag helps students find and differentiate this game from others you might also have in your math area. It also helps to glue the cards onto oaktag and then laminate them or use clear contact paper to protect them. If you want to be fancy, you can use sheets of wallpaper on the back, under the oaktag, to give each card a pretty backing. Although it takes time the first time you do this, the cards will be durable and will last several years. [If you make all of your math games durably and marked you can store them in milk carton crates and the children can independently get what they need whenever you use games during math workshop.]

How to Play:

❖ This game is played a bit like the card game WAR (sometimes also known as Compare).

❖ Players begin by shuffling the cards and dealing them out to all players.

❖ On each turn, players turn over one card from their pile so that both partners can see the numbers. The player who has the greatest value on his or her card takes both cards and determines where they go on the line.

❖ Players discuss and come to agreement about approximately where the cards go. Then they place the cards on the line with paper clips. **HOWEVER**, if the players have equivalent values on their cards, they must discuss why they are equivalent. When they agree, those equivalent cards get paper-clipped together as a pair and go into the plastic bag. **ALSO,** if a card is played at any time that is equivalent to something on the line, its match gets removed from the line and the pair goes into the bag. The remaining card is placed on the line.

❖ Play continues in this manner until all the cards are played.

❖ After all cards have been played, the pairs in the bag are counted. The goal is to get as many pairs in the bag as possible. That number of pairs is the team's score. Players can keep track of their score so that each time they play, they can try to improve on their previous score.

Supporting the Investigation

As students are playing, move around the room and see what fractions they know to be equivalent and which ones they are challenged by. Be sure to check in with the students you noted during the minilesson who may need support to play the game. Students should be talking about the cards before they are placed on the line or in the bag, justifying their decisions. Remind them how mathematicians always have to justify or prove their thinking to others. They don't just guess. They want to be certain. Note student strategies as you are observing and checking in. This is also a good opportunity for you to document their learning by taking a picture of their work. The New Perspectives on Assessment web-based app (www.NewPerspectivesOnAssessment.com) is an ideal way to do this. You can even take a quick 30-second video!

If you like, towards the end of math workshop you can have students come together in the meeting area to share strategies they found helpful as they played and fractions they found difficult or couldn't find a pair for. A discussion on the fractions that challenged some students will be helpful as others share the fractions that could have been matched and why. [Note: Every fraction in the deck has a pair.]

Reflections on the Day

On Day Nine of this ten-day unit, students should show a much deeper understanding of how fractions relate to each other and what equivalent fractions represent. They should have strategies they can use to compare fractions and place them in order. With the minilesson, students had the opportunity to think about how fractions are numbers between 0 and 1. Most likely, this minilesson was a nice support as students moved into playing the game. As you observed and supported the students during the game, you were able to see strategies and discussion based on what they learned over the course of the unit. This was an opportune time to see the progress students have made, to celebrate it with them, and to record their progress on the landscape of learning.

DAY TEN

REFLECTING ON THE LEARNING

Today students begin math workshop with the construction of a number line for fractions. After comparing answers and sharing their insights as to where the fractions go on the line, students reflect on their work throughout the unit and provide reflections they will share with the class and their community on a "learning scroll."

Day Ten Outline

Minilesson

❖ Two students hold a piece of twine (or clothesline) stretched out, one on each end. Using the cards from the game played the previous day, the class discusses one card at a time and places each on the line.

Constructing the Learning Scroll

❖ Convene students at the meeting area to discuss how their ideas about fractions and measurement evolved over the course of the last two weeks.

Materials Needed

Students' work from the unit

Bulletin board paper, prepared with pictures of the students, cutouts of conversation bubbles, and other pictures of the students at work

Reflection prompts

Pencils and Markers

A set of the cards used on Day Nine for the game *Bag It or Hang It?*

20 clothespins (clip style) and a box of paperclips

A piece of strong twine or clothesline approximately 6 feet long

---

Minilesson: A group fraction line

Choose two students to hold a piece of clothesline (or strong twine), one on each end. Explain that the line is a portion of a number line that goes from 0 to 1, and that you have some cards that you want to hang on the line. Explain that you will show one card at a time and everyone should consider where it goes, showing with a thumbs up when they think they know. Remind students that as mathematicians, they will also need to provide a convincing argument. Once there is group consensus, hang the card on the line with a clothespin. With two children holding the ends of the line, it will be possible to use the folding strategies students have developed. For example, if someone says that 1/2 goes in the middle, the rope can be folded to find the exact middle and then the card can be pinned at that point on the line. The rope should then be stretched out as a line again before another card is placed.

When a new card is equivalent to another already hanging, use a paper clip to attach it below the first card as shown in the figure below:

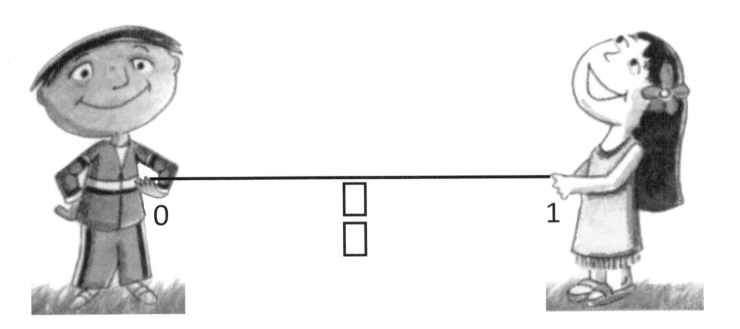

Building the Learning Scroll

A learning scroll is a class display—a sort of " socio-historical" wall—documenting the progression of the unit, children's questions, the important ideas constructed over the past two weeks, samples of students' work, and descriptions of their strategies and ideas, including anecdotes of how their thinking may have changed over time. It is a document of the progression and emergence of learning over the past two weeks for the purpose of reflection. By making this display available, you allow your students to revisit and reflect on all the wonderful ideas and strategies that emerged as they worked throughout the unit. Your third graders may need you to scaffold some of this reflection work, but they should be able to partner in identifying and describing their thoughts and strategies.

In preparation for today's work, use a roll of chart paper and cut out a long length sufficient to cover a bulletin board or a display area in a hallway. Curl and staple the two ends, making a small roll on each end to make it look like a scroll. Staple or tape the scroll to the area to be covered. At the top of the scroll put the title: Building Benches and Measuring Tools. On the left you might begin with a picture of the first bench if you actually built benches. If you didn't build them, you might just hang a strip that the students measured on Day One with a few samples of children's work, and post a copy of Appendix A. If you took pictures of students at work, put a few of them up and use a picture of one of the students saying (in the conversation bubble), "We measured in feet but the bench needed to be longer. We folded the foot and realized it was 1/2 a foot longer, and that was 6 inches more!" Continue documenting the progression of the learning that occurred by selectively picking key pieces of children's work from the ten days of the unit and include these on a pathway from left to right, leaving plenty of blank space for anecdotes and explanations. You can use speech bubbles all along the way to show insights students had about fractions, or even ideas they may have had that were eventually disproved.

You may want to provide templates with some empty speech bubbles with prompts like "At first I thought…" "Then I realized…" and "A good strategy was…" Attach these student explanations to the learning scroll. Wherever you can, show the developmental emergence of ideas on the landscape in the Overview. Display the scroll somewhere that students, and hopefully also the wider school community, will be able to revisit and reflect on their learning in the weeks to come.

Reflections on the Unit

The word fraction stems from the Latin verb *fractio,* which means to break apart. Initially, only unit fractions existed. Unit fractions have numerators of 1. Historically, fractions were seen as the breaking apart (the division) of the whole into equal pieces. Common fractions as we know them today (for example, 3/4, where the numerator is not 1) were not invented until the 17th century.

In this unit, your children have had many opportunities to explore and measure lengths that required them to break apart the whole (the foot strip) into equal pieces in order to measure more exactly. In doing so, they invented fractions. You have been witnessing this evolution firsthand. Note the landscape depicted on the graphic in the Overview. Your students were introduced to fractions by dividing a foot into equal smaller lengths because the tool they were using needed to be divided into equal, smaller pieces for more exactness. As your young mathematicians worked, they constructed many big ideas about fractions: if the numerators are one, the bigger the denominator, the smaller the piece; to halve a fraction double the denominator; fractions come from division and can be represented as such; and the whole matters! They explored the relationships between some landmark fractions: 1/4 = 1/2 of 1/2 and 1/8 = 1/2 of 1/4. Students used a double number line to represent equivalent measurements such as: 3 x 1/4 = 3/4 and 3/4 of 12 = 9, so 9/12 = 3/4. 1/2 of a foot is 6 inches, so 6/12 = 1/2. As they explored how 6/12 could be seen as 6 x 1/12 they were inventing common fractions!

The *Building Benches and Measuring Tools* unit also provided your students with opportunities to consider the relationship between multiplication and division. As your developing mathematicians progress further on the landscape for fractions in the years to come, the foundation they have been building over the last two weeks with you will be a powerful asset.

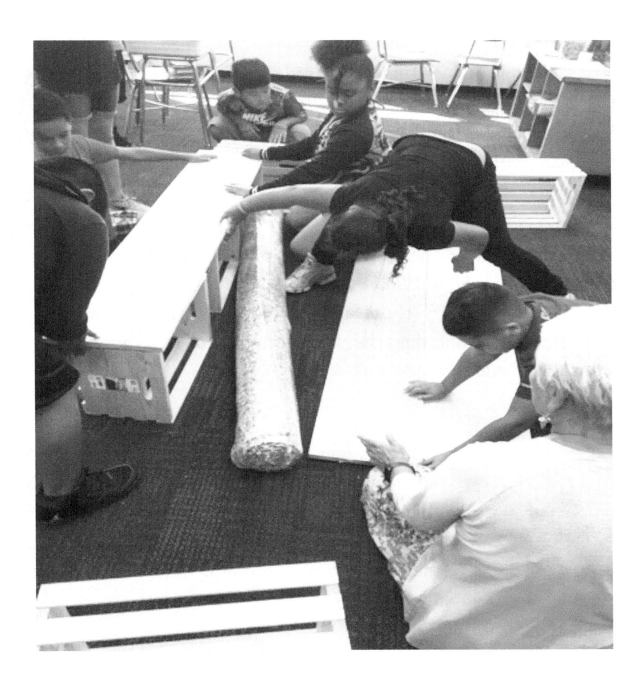

Appendix A – Building Benches

Tanisha and Tamika are best friends. They live next door to each other and have played together every day since they were babies. Now they are in the same classes at school! Last year Mrs. Washington was their teacher and she was always finding fun math problems for them to do. "Investigations," Mrs. Washington called them.

In the beginning of the year, Tamika and Tanisha helped Mrs. Washington build a blueprint with measurements on it so she could measure and make signs for a school art show. Tamika had thought of the idea. She brought a roll of adding machine paper to school, and all of the kids measured the art papers with connecting cubes and then they turned the roll of paper into a measuring strip with all their measurements marked on it.

Tanisha's dad, Mr. Arnold, is a carpenter and when he learned about what Tanisha and Tamika had done, he got out his carpenter's tape measure to show them. "It sounds like you are making a measuring tool like mine," he said as he showed them his carpenter's tape measure.

The girls loved all of the carpentry tools Mr. Arnold had and one day Tanisha asked her dad if he would help them to build a toolbox like his, but out of wood.

They built a toolbox together, and Tanisha's dad even bought her a new tool belt like his where she could carry a hammer, a tape measure, and other smaller tools.

The girls were so excited that they worked on carpentry projects together all summer. Now the girls are in third grade. Their new teacher, Mr. Sanchez, decided it would be nice to build some benches for the meeting area in their classroom, where they have their math congresses to talk about their strategies for problems.

The girls offered to help, but soon they were faced with a real dilemma. They needed to give Mr. Arnold the measurements so he could purchase and cut the boards, and Mr. Sanchez showed them the length he wanted so they could measure it. They tried measuring with their tape measure but the tape measure was too short and did not span the full length. They tried adding one foot more at the end of the tape measure using a ruler, but this measurement was now too long.

What do you think they should they do? Mr. Arnold needs an exact measurement, not an estimation. He needs to know *exactly* the right place to cut. And he needs to know what length boards to buy. The boards only come in 6-foot, 8-foot, and 10-foot lengths. What lengths should he buy and where should he cut?

$^1/_2$	$^2/_4$	$^1/_3$	$^4/_{12}$
$^1/_4$	$^1/_2 + ^1/_4$	$^3/_4$	$^3/_{12}$

$6/12$	$1/2$	$2/3$	$4/1$
$1/2$ of $1/4$	$3/3$	1	$8/12$
$1/8$	$4/4$	$1/2 + 1/2$	4

Made in the USA
Las Vegas, NV
06 October 2021